The Future
of
Soil Science

International Union of Soil Sciences

CIP-Gegevens Koninklijke Bibliotheek, Den Haag

© IUSS 2006
PO Box 353, 6700 AJ Wageningen, The Netherlands

The Future of Soil Science / edited by Alfred E. Hartemink (1964).
Wageningen: IUSS International Union of Soil Sciences.

ISBN 90-71556-16-6

...if you gaze for long into an abyss,
the abyss gazes also into you

Friedrich Nietzsche
Beyond Good and Evil, Aphorism 146
German philosopher (1844 - 1900)

Table of contents

♦

Foreword

For any scientific discipline it is good to look back and make out what has been achieved, how it was done and whether anything can be learned from the past. No doubt that is a respectable activity but it will not yield scientific breakthroughs. If you want to stay in business as a science it is healthier to look forward. Soil scientists have attempted to look back as well as ahead. Most soil scientists are not accurate and professional historians (not surprisingly as most scientists aren't) so looking back should be perhaps be left to those who can distinguish significant trends from individual preconceived notions. What about looking forward? Well, that is what this book is all about.

Shifts in research foci, tertiary education and government support for the sciences have caused a reduction in the number of soil scientists and soil science departments but, also, offered many new opportunities. That happened in many parts of the world although not everywhere at the same magnitude. Change has not stopped; more is on its way. Ignoring these changes would be imprudent.

In the past decades there have been several papers on the role and future of soil science in a rapidly changing world. Most of these papers have an individual perspective on a specific topic, country, or issue confronting soil science or a group of soil scientists. A brief, but far from complete, analysis of some of the main papers is given below focusing on the soil science identity, funding, directions for the future in different countries, and the environmental and agricultural aspects of soil research.

Firstly, there are more than a few papers that question what soil is and how the identity of the soil science discipline relates to the subject of its study and the other sciences including the basic and applied aspects of research (e.g. Gardner, 1991; Hudson, 1992; Jacob and Nordt, 1991; Leeper, 1965; Ruellan, 1997; Wild, 1989). There is a tradition of discussing the issue of pedology vs. soil science also in relation to the soil science identity (Churchward, 1988; Daniels, 1988; Dobrovolskii, 1999; Miller, 1993; Stephens, 1954; Vance, 1998). Starting in the 1980s, several papers have dealt with the shift of focus in soil science from agriculture to broader environmental aspects (Gardner, 1993; Greenland, 1991; Hillel, 1993; Menzel, 1991; Tinker, 1985; Warkentin, 1994).

Despite the importance of external funding as a result of withdrawing government support, few papers focus solely on the funding of soil science (Mermut and Eswaran, 1997; Satchell, 1992; Stephens, 2003) although funding and future trends are also treated in some other papers (Bouma, 1997; Hartemink, 2001; Nielsen, 1987; Ruellan et al., 1997).

There are also various national examples e.g. Russia (Dobrovolskii, 2001), New Zealand (Cameron, 1994; Clothier, 2004), United Kingdom (Greenwood, 1993), Netherlands (Bouma and Hartemink, 2002), Australia (Gilkes, 2004) and more general viewpoints for the tropics (Lal, 2000; Sanchez, 1994; Theng, 1991).

In the past 20 years there have been suggestions for a new type of soil scientist (Warkentin, 1999), a new type of soil science that is more holistic (Bridges and Catizzone, 1996), part of a network society (Bouma, 2001), geared towards a soil care approach (Yaalon, 1996) or in closer relation with society (McCracken, 1987; Simonson, 1991; Yaalon and Arnold, 2000).

These papers have been widely read (rarely quoted) and contain sometimes conflicting views and ideas on the future of soil science; some are confident on the future whereas others present a fairly negative outlook. In order to actualise views on the future of soil science, I invited 98 colleagues around the world to write their ideas in about 1,000 words. I felt that a document was needed to feed the discussion of the pessimists ("pedology is dead and buried") and the optimists ("future for soil science is brighter than ever"), and that would also make background reading for the 18th World Congress of Soil Science in Philadelphia, USA.

Colleagues in all continents and with different backgrounds were contacted; some were young, some were old, some work in applied soil science, others do more fundamental work. More than half responded and a handful of contributions were unsuitable. It took more than 650 e-mail messages and some slash-and-burn editing to get to this book that gives the views of 55 soil scientists from 28 countries. There is some imbalance in geographical distribution; from some countries all requests yielded a publishable view on the future, whereas authors from several countries never responded or failed to deliver. That is regrettable, but let us assume they had more imperative things to do than to contemplate about the future of soil science, and that their absent views are not overlooked in the other contributions.

I thank all the authors for their most interesting contributions and the timely delivery of their articles. Dr David Dent of ISRIC – World Soil Information is thanked for his editing of this introduction, the epilogue and my own contribution (written before I read all others).

I trust this book will serve its purpose: that it will be read, but more importantly, I hope it will stimulate some thinking. With a bit of luck this book encourages both, and if it doesn't: try the Rodin pose but don't gaze too long.

Alfred Hartemink
Deputy Secretary General IUSS
Amsterdam-Wageningen, April 2006

References

Bouma, J., 1997. The role of quantitative approaches in soil science when interacting with stakeholders. Geoderma, 78: 1-12.

Bouma, J., 2001. The new role of soil science in a network society. Soil Science, 166: 874-879.

Bouma, J. and Hartemink, A.E., 2002. Soil science and society in the Dutch context. Netherlands Journal of Agricultural Science, 50: 133-140.

Bridges, E.M. and Catizzone, M., 1996. Soil science in a holistic framework - Discussion of an improved integrated approach. Geoderma, 71: 275-287.

Cameron, K.C., 1994. Metamorphism of soil science: an exciting future ahead. New Zealand Soil News: 176-186.

Churchward, M., 1988. Whither field pedology. Australian Soils News, 75: 94-95.

Clothier, B.E., 2004. Soil science in New Zealand: requiem or renaissance? SuperSoil 2004. 3rd Australian New Zealand Soils Conference, University of Sydney, Australia.

Daniels, R.B., 1988. Pedology, a field or laboratory science? Soil Science Society of America Journal, 52: 1518-1519.

Dobrovolskii, G.V., 1999. Modern pedology and its role in science and life. Eurasian Soil Science, 32: 5-9.

Dobrovolskii, G.V., 2001. Soil science at the turn of the century: Results and challenges. Eurasian Soil Science, 34: 115-119.

Gardner, W.R., 1991. Soil science as a basic science. Soil Science, 151: 2-6.

Gardner, W.R., 1993. A call to action. Soil Science Society of America Journal, 57: 1403-1405.

Gilkes, R.J., 2004. After more than a century of Australian research, why do we still mismanage our soil and water? SuperSoil 2004. 3rd Australian New Zealand Soils Conference, University of Sydney, Australia.

Greenland, D.J., 1991. The contributions of soil science to society - past, present, and future. Soil Science, 151: 19-23.

Greenwood, D.J., 1993. The changing scene of British soil science. Journal of Soil Science, 44: 191-207.

Hartemink, A.E., 2001. Publish or perish (5) Soil science for business. Bulletin of the International Union of Soil Sciences, 99: 50-59.

Hillel, D., 1993. Science and the crisis of the environment. Geoderma, 60: 377-382.

Hudson, B.D., 1992. The soil survey as paradigm-based science. Soil Science Society of America Journal, 56: 836-841.

Jacob, J.S. and Nordt, L.C., 1991. Soil and landscape evolution: a paradigm for pedology. Soil Science Society of America Journal, 55: 1194.

Lal, R., 2000. Physical management of soils of the tropics: Priorities for the 21st century. Soil Science, 165: 191-207.

Leeper, G.W., 1965. Soil science is a discipline in itself. Soils and Fertilizers, 2: 99-100.

McCracken, R.J., 1987. Soils, soil scientists, and civilization. Soil Science Society of America Journal, 51: 1395-1400.

Menzel, R.G., 1991. Soil science: the environmental challenge. Soil Science, 151: 24-29.

Mermut, A.R. and Eswaran, H., 1997. Opportunities for soil science in a milieu of reduced funds. Canadian Journal of Soil Science, 77: 1-7.

Miller, F.P., 1993. Soil science: a scope broader than its identity. Soil Science Society of America Journal, 57: 299-300.

Nielsen, D.R., 1987. Emerging frontiers in soil science. Geoderma, 40: 267-273.

Ruellan, A., 1997. Some reflections on the scientific basis of soil science. Eurasian Soil Science (Pochvovedenie), 30: 347-349.

Ruellan, A., Heuvelink, G.B.M., Brown, R.B., Culley, J. and White, R.E., 1997. The role of quantitative approaches in soil science when interacting with stakeholders - Discussion. Geoderma, 78: 13-24.

Sanchez, P.A., 1994. Tropical soil fertility research: towards the second paradigm, Transactions 15th World Congress of Soil Science. ISSS, Acapulco, pp. 65-88.

Satchell, J., 1992. Take the money - call the tune. Soil Biology and Biochemistry, 24: 1193-1196.

Simonson, R.W., 1991. Soil science - Goals for the next 75 years. Soil Science, 151: 7-18.

Stephens, C.G., 1954. The scientific and social philosophy of the pedologist. The Journal of Australian Institute of Agricultural Science, 20: 9-12.

Stephens, P., 2003. Soil research and funding cuts. NZ Soil News: 76-77.

Theng, B.K.G., 1991. Soil science in the tropics - The next 75 years. Soil Science, 151: 76-90.

Tinker, P.B., 1985. Soil science in a changing world. J. of Soil Sci., 36: 1-8.

Vance, G.F., 1998. What is a soil scientist? ASSSI Profile, 113: 10-11.

Warkentin, B.P., 1994. The discipline of soil science - How should it be organized. Soil Science Society of America Journal, 58: 267-268.

Warkentin, B.P., 1999. The return of the "other" soil scientists. Canadian Journal of Soil Science, 79: 1-4.

Wild, A., 1989. Soil scientists as members of the scientific community. Journal of Soil Science, 40: 209-221.

Yaalon, D.H., 1996. Soil science in transition - Soil awareness and soil care research strategies. Soil Science, 161: 3-8.

Yaalon, D.H. and Arnold, R.W., 2000. Attitudes toward soils and their societal relevance: Then and now. Soil Science, 165: 5-12.

♦

Soil science through field glasses

Darwin Anderson
Department of Soil Science, University of Saskatchewan, Saskatoon, SK, S7N 5A8, Canada. E-mail andersd@duke.usask.ca

The invitation to comment on the "Future of Soil Science" is an opportunity to discuss some of the trends and possibilities that have been on my mind and in conversations with colleagues, with the additional requirement of actually putting words to paper, a welcome opportunity. To prepare, I have not read (in most cases, re-read) the several thoughtful articles on the future of our science, nor have a lot of statistics been consulted. These are my thoughts and opinions as a pedologist of more than 40 years experience, conditioned by that experience but with an eye to the future.

Certain metaphors or analogies seem appropriate, including three with a 'glass' theme. The phrase "Now we see through a glass darkly" as attributed to the Apostle Paul comes to mind, implying an obscure or imperfect view of reality. My view is bound to be not perfect, in that it is personal with limitations based on experience, but hopefully not obscure. Another phrase 'to see the world through rose-coloured glasses', suggests that the view may not be realistic, seeing something of a fantasy world. I trust that this is not the case, although it is easy to go there. The analogy that is preferred is one of 'field glasses', or binoculars. Field glasses magnify and bring objects closer, but within the context of the entire field of view, the landscape. They focus on the object of interest, as part of the larger world in which the object exists. Field glasses are an appropriate metaphor, in that the theme of my discussion is that soil science must remain, perhaps even become more that way, a science based on the study of real soils in nature with all the related complexities and mystery, if we are to continue as a valued natural science.

The study of soil will endure as long as long as the soil and the civilizations that depend on the soil endure. Bigger questions may well be, will soil science as a recognized branch of natural science be still around, and will soil scientists as we know them today be doing those studies? Perhaps soil science is constrained by its own history and heritage. If soil science has parents, they are most probably chemistry and geology. Early successes were in mineralogy, weathering, soil formation, soil classification, soil chemistry and fertility. Today, as evinced by several articles in "Soil: The Final Frontier", the special issue of Science (2004), the focus is on soil and biotic processes, including soil and humankind.

Well-researched papers heard at recent conferences are at the root of my concerns. The papers were presented by scientists with expertise in biology or ecology and take a refreshing look at soil that focus mainly on the life in the soil and the connections to the above ground biota. The scientists are exploring the black box that soil used to be to them. Involving a pedologist may well have set the studies more firmly in the ever larger worlds of the horizon, the pedon, the landscape and so on, but they are essentially good studies that resulted in excellent and informed discussion.

Soil porosity was the topic of a recent lecture at my University. Porosity was defined and calculations were made relating porosity to bulk density, and so on. What was missed was that it is the pore space, and more specifically the water films in the pores that are the spaces used by life in the soil. Pore space is where the action is!

There will be considerable progress, as there has been in recent decades, in applying ever more sophisticated technologies to measuring or identifying things in the soil. This is well-illustrated by studies of soil humus, where methods developed in chemistry and biochemistry are being applied with great success. Solid-state NMR and various synchrotron-based spectroscopies come to mind, and many others. I see these new methods as being in their first stages of application, where the elegance of the method has been the focus. The new technologies will really bear fruit when the method becomes well-tested and the comparison of related groups of soils or conditions becomes the theme. Progress must be based on new understanding, not just on papers published.

Soil scientists are asked increasingly for input into real problems, putting science to work in developing policy and regulation. Nutrient management and land reclamation are good examples of the past few decades. Global change and more specifically responding to national programs related to the Kyoto protocol are present challenges. Policy makers require best possible estimates of greenhouse gas emissions and carbon sequestration, scaled up with soil survey maps and data. Estimates are needed, even when the science may not be done to our level of comfort. It is important that those with the best knowledge be involved, or the work will be done by others.

We soil scientists must do better at communicating our science to others. People must know and appreciate soils if the land and its biota are to be sustained. Hans Jenny (1984) commented, in "My Friend, The Soil", that soil scientists often speak in a language foreign to most, stressing the technical details, using our own jargon. The elegant functions of soil, the beauty, even the mystery and our reverence for soil are generally not part of the discussion. One of the best teachers in soil science at my University is described by students as being able to take a dull subject and make it interesting, a considerable accomplishment even if reflecting a negative idea about soil. In the already mentioned special issue, Soil: The Final Frontier, McNeill and Winiwarter (2004, p 1629) write "Soil ecosystems remain firmly but uncharismatically at the foundations of human life". In future, soil scientists must move beyond our many technical accomplishments, making soils more interesting, more alive and vital to ourselves, our students, the larger science community, and the community broadly defined. It is a daunting task, but the challenge is well worth the effort.

References

Jenny, H., 1984. My friend, the soil. J. Soil and Water Conservation 39: 158-161.

McNeill, J.R. and V. Winiwarter, 2004. Breaking the sod: humankind, history and soil. Science 304:1627-1629.

♦

The future of soil science

Olafur Arnalds
Agricultural University of Iceland, Faculty of Environmental Sciences, Keldnaholt, 112, Reykjavik, Iceland. E-mail oa@lbhi.is

Human civilization is deeply rooted in the use of soils, while soil science as a discipline is surprisingly young. It began less than two centuries ago, closely linked to geography, geology and botanical sciences. The role of soils as a medium for food production soon became the focus of soil science, establishing one of the pillars of agricultural sciences, which is still standing solid. Soil science was included in university entities devoted to agricultural sciences under various designations. In the Second World War in Europe and many other parts of the world including the USA, food security became a major influence on the development of soil science during the last century. Soil science was in part integrated with the science of agronomy and cultivation of soils. During this period, great advancement was made within the many topics of soil science, such as in chemistry, physics, mineralogy, genesis, conservation and plant nutrition - and food safety was achieved in the industrialized countries. Sufficient food production was also ensured by diverting other national resources to agriculture through various forms of subsidies. This effort has not ensured food for all people; it has in part had a negative effect on agriculture in many less developed countries.

The present

The role and status of soil science as a discipline is currently a substantial consideration. There are perhaps reasons for concern; the number of students entering research based university programs is declining in many areas. Subjects that require knowledge of soils in various environmental sciences and tasks are being addressed by other than soil scientists. A sign of a negative spiral has surfaced in universities, a dwindling number of students with a decreasing number of soil science faculties.

When food production was no longer a security issue in the industrialized countries, the crop-oriented soil science programs were slow to respond. Has soil science as a profession been lacking dynamics to adjust to change? In part at least; soil science was slow to embrace its role as an environmental science. I think that soil science has somewhat been stuck in the agronomic paradigm, perhaps understandably so, crop production being by far the biggest industry in the world and one of the foundations of culture and society. Soil science, however, too often regards the soil as an entity in itself, rather than as a part of ecosystems that provide services to mankind, such as the water cycle and nutrient cycle, not to mention the vegetation. This is especially true when considering natural or semi-natural systems used for grazing or areas covered with forests.

It is worth noting how the soil as a resource is poorly cared for under international conventions, in spite of its importance. The UN Convention on desertification (CCD) is based on regional development politics rather than sound scientific background, and it is disadvantaged by conceptual problems. Soils are extremely important in the global cycle of carbon. Still, consideration of soils was slow to emerge in the context of the UN Framework Convention of Climate Change (FCCC). Soil scientists will undoubtedly play an increasingly important role in understanding the global carbon cycle and to point out ways to reduce carbon dioxide levels in the atmosphere by storing carbon in ecosystems and producing bio-fuel. But the soil science community needs also to increase the visibility of soils in international environmental and political context.

The future

What lies in the future for soil science? The time has come for soil science to mature, to cut the umbilical cord that ties soil science to agronomy. Soil science deserves a place as an academic discipline in itself in the university system. As such, it can meet the multiple needs of many other disciplines for soil science knowledge. New frontiers include microbiology and biochemistry, which are casting new light on biodiversity, soil-plant interactions and the fate of chemicals in ecosystems. Human health issues call for increased activity linking soils and geochemistry, while soil- and water conservation issues are already demanding more attention in most parts of the world. With severely degraded areas growing each day, ecological restoration, one of the fastest growing subject of science today, will become more important, a discipline where soil science plays a major role. Soil science will continue to be important for dealing with global change and maintaining biodiversity. The future calls for more interaction of soil scientists with professionals of other disciplines for obtaining more comprehensive understanding of the Earth's ecosystems.

One important aspect is that the human pressure on soil and water resources will increase with a growing population. The threats are numerous and well documented and include loss of organic matter and fertility, erosion, pollution, losses to urban development, losses of soil functions and services such as water storage and nutrient cycling. Even though the soil scientist has done well in characterizing these problems, he or she has not done as well in getting the message clear to the general public and administrations. The future health of soils calls for more involvement of soil scientists towards sustainable development; we need to value such services as much as peer reviewed publications. The future of soil science will open up new horizons of scientific endeavours as well as services to the inhabitants of our planet Earth.

♦

Future of soil science

Dick Arnold
9311 Coronado Terrace, Fairfax, VA 22031-3835, USA. E-mail ct9311@aol.com

We are slowly recognizing that the Earth does not understand good intentions − nor does it care that we did not mean to do harm, or that we promise not to do it again. The Earth records actions − the flow of energy and materials. That's all.

Speaking about the flow of materials, have you ever considered that the carbon atoms in your body are recycled? Where they were before you, and before that, is not known with any degree of certainty. The biogeochemical cycles that constantly shape our planet include all things biotic and abiotic. For many eons they continued without major impacts of human activity, but that is no longer true.

Modern civilization is dependent on the managed exploitation of terrestrial ecosystems. The basic need for food, feed, fibre, and fuel has been surpassed by an insatiable desire for more and more material goods. This excessive consumption pattern now permeates civilization and we are in the throes of the "tragedy of the global commons". It is a man-made circumstance, commonly exacerbated by catastrophic natural events, but not caused by them. Thus, the challenge for civilization is to reconcile the demands of human development with the tolerances of nature.

Sustainable integration of societal desires and natural resources is commonly jeopardized. Natural landscapes consist of intricately integrated components both spatially and temporally. Through the interaction of internal processes responding to external forces a dynamic, quasi-equilibrium is achieved as rapidly as possible. This stability of natural ecosystems we associate with their sustainability. Most man-made environments have lost the balance of natural ecosystem functions that once sustained them.

Agriculture, grazing, and forestry are invasive activities, and highly disruptive of natural ecosystems. The regenerative capacity of soils under natural conditions is less and slower than needed by modern society. When soils are stressed beyond their limits of resilience they are unable to return to their former productive states without massive external inputs. Agriculture continues as the basic activity linking entire social systems in a web of production, distribution, and consumption. The foundation of sustainable agriculture is a healthy resource base and a balanced relationship between production and system maintenance.

Soil science operates simultaneously in the realms of ecology and economics, each of which marks time by different clocks. Numerous aspects of science and those of sociology are crucial to the relevance and value of soil science. The role of soils can be viewed as a set of trade-offs among the various functions of soils as determined by current society. If conservation and rational use of soil resources are not important enough for society in the next few decades, then the trade-offs may keep us headed toward the "tragedy of the global commons". If, however, the trade-offs are for planetary sustainability, then the opportunities are golden for imparting the knowledge and wisdom of soil science.

How do we learn things? What does it take for words, sights, sounds, touch, taste, and feelings to become part of us? It takes psychological reactions as well as physiological ones, and to learn we must be tuned in to messages and have hooks, or niches, to hold them. If we understand more about how we learn, then there are possibilities for us to learn how to teach better so that others may learn.

You and I know that soils are not human, but we still like to give them some anthropogenic characteristics from time to time.

> *Hello there, folks. Do you know who or what I am? I am the geomembrane of the Earth. I am your protective filter, your buffer, your mediator of energy, water, and biogeochemical compounds. I am your sustainer of productive life, your ultimate source of elements, and the habitat for most biota. I am the foundation that supports you, the cradle of your myths, and the dust to which you will return. I am a soil.*

Soils are so common and taken-for-granted that we seldom are aware of many of their attributes that affect our daily lives. Soils are complex systems and as such, possess attributes common to most systems, including these: resistance – an ability to maintain current conditions; residence time – the capacity to store and release compounds; productivity – the capability for plant growth and yield; resilience – recovery from disturbance; responsiveness – the capacity for external enhancement; flexibility – the multiplicity of uses related to properties; and sustainability – a dynamic equilibrium of interactions.

If we have learned the right things, we ought to be able to be in a position to do the right things with that knowledge. The leap from knowledge to actions, however, is often a large one. Lin Yutang said, "Don't be afraid to take a big step if one is indicated. You can't cross a chasm in two small jumps."

As soil scientists we have a responsibility, an obligation, to help people understand soils. You will find many compelling ideas in these writings about the future of soil science. We need to keep expressing our interpretations of facts and circumstances – it is the right thing to do.

References

Arnold, R.W., 2002. Role of soils in the 21st century. In: Lal., R. (ed) Encyclopedia of soil science. Marcel Dekker, New York. p 1353-1356

Brown, L.R., 2006. Plan B 2.0: rescuing a planet under stress and a civilization in trouble. WW Norton & Co., New York.

Gardner, G., Assadourian, E. and Sarin, R., 2004. The state of consumption today. In: Worldwatch Institute, State of the World 2004. WW Norton & Co., New York. p 3-21

German Advisory Council on Global Change, 1995. World in Transition: the Threat to Soils. 1994 Annual Report; Economia, Verlag, Bonn.

Meadows, D.H., Randers, J. and Meadows, D.L., 2004. Limits to growth: the 30 year update. Chelsea Green Pub. Co., White river Junction, VT.

♦

A vision for the future of soil science

Philippe Baveye

Department of Crop and Soil Sciences, Bradfield Hall, Cornell University, Ithaca, New York 14853, USA. E-mail Philippe.Baveye@Cornell.edu

Soil science is in crisis. Every few months, it seems, another soil science department changes its name to one in which the word "soil" no longer appears. Growing numbers of researchers are also lobbying for newly-concocted expressions like "hydropedology" or "critical zone science" to replace the allegedly outmoded appellation of "soil science". These trends are concomitant with a sharp decrease in the clientele of most soil science programs (Baveye et al., 2006). Results of institutional and graduate student surveys carried out in 1992 and 2004 indicate that enrolment in M.Sc. and Ph.D. programs in soil science in U.S. and Canadian universities has dropped on average by about 40% during the past decade. Similar declines are also manifest in other countries. In terms of publications, even though the number of peer-reviewed articles on soils-related issues published every year has grown exponentially in the last two decades, less than 15% of these articles are authored by individuals who are affiliated with a research unit that includes the term "soil" or "soils" in its name. Clearly, all of these statistics indicate that the discipline of soil science is losing market share and visibility at an alarming pace.

If this trend continues unabated, a situation may soon ensue where soil-related issues will be dealt with only by engineers, ecologists, chemists or physicists, all of them well-intentioned, but lacking proper training in soil science, and in particular lacking a satisfactory understanding of the complex nature of soils. Chemists will continue to apply the principles of chemistry and ever more sophisticated analytical tools to soils, and others will do similarly from the vantage point of their own disciplinary base. They will be largely repeating what at least some soil scientists used to do decades ago, when soil physicists playing with glass beads and soil chemists working with "reagent grade" soils, stored for years in small bottles in their laboratories, were applying to them simple theories developed for far simpler systems than soils. However, soil scientists have since graduated from these reductive perspectives on soils, and now recognize that almost all soil issues have complex and interwoven physical, chemical, biological and mineralogical aspects, which imperatively require an *integrative approach* and simultaneous expertise in *all* of the relevant fundamental disciplines. Sooner or later, it is likely that non-soil scientists dabbling with soil issues will face insurmountable obstacles in their work, and will also, eventually, awake to the realization that a holistic approach is needed. This reinvention of soil science, if by then our discipline has virtually disappeared from the radar screen, may take decades.

Fortunately, there are alternate avenues for soil science to have a bright future in the less distant future. Survey analyses and interviews with past students suggest that one key reason for the current decline of graduate soil science education is the insistence of many soil scientists and some scholarly societies to limit the scope of our discipline to a strictly agricultural context. The dangers inherent in this myopic perspective were enunciated clearly by Marbut (1921): "Probably more harm has been done to the science by the almost universal attempt to look upon the soil merely as a producer of crops rather than as a natural body worthy in and for itself of all the study that can be devoted to it, than most men realize. The science has undoubtedly been retarded in its development by this attitude". Some eighty years after this assessment was written, it rings truer than ever, in many respects.

To broaden the scope and appeal of our discipline beyond its agricultural confines, and to insure for it a bright future, a number of practical things can be done. In fact, steps are being taken in those directions already by various individuals.

A first area of action concerns the education of students at the university and, before that, at all stages of their earlier schooling. A few of us in North America recently started teaching lower-level undergraduate courses, entitled "Soils and civilizations" or a variant thereof. These courses have been received with amazing enthusiasm across the board, including by students majoring in Fine Arts or Arts and Sciences. In these courses, students are introduced to the close connections that have existed historically between the rise and fall of many civilizations and, respectively, positive uses or misuses of soils and land resources. Students are often surprised to discover that soils can affect their life directly in many ways other than through crop production. The same message should be conveyed to younger students, starting in kindergarten.

Besides this educational endeavour, the study of many non-agricultural topics would heighten dramatically the visibility of our discipline. One immediately thinks of the topical environmental issues of the day, like global warming and the availability of adequate groundwater resources, which deserve the involvement of larger numbers of soil scientists, since soils play a key role in these problems. Soil scientists can also contribute significantly to other issues, which should not be left to non-soil scientists to tackle. One good example is the contamination of urban soils. By far the majority of the world's population lives in urban and suburban areas, where people are potentially exposed to soil-borne contaminants and pathogens via a range of pathways including inhalation, ingestion and dermal contact, either of soil directly, of the soil-derived dust that finds its way in people's homes, or of produce grown in the soils (*e.g.*, in suburban gardens).

Another topic on which significantly more research should be carried out by soil scientists than is the case now, concerns possible links between soils and animal or human health. The case of fatal neurodegenerative diseases like "scrapie" in sheep, Creutzfeldt-Jakob disease (CJD) in humans, and chronic wasting disease (CWD) in deers, is particularly interesting in this respect. Detailed investigations of scrapie, CJD, and CWD clusters in Iceland, Slovakia and Colorado, respectively, have shown that soils in these regions tend to be significantly lower in copper and higher in manganese than average, and researchers have hypothesized that this imbalance might be closely linked to the onset of the diseases. Similar observations have been made for other diseases. Rarely have soil scientists been involved in these studies, to which they could however contribute so significantly.

As a "take-home" message, I firmly believe that as soon as soil scientists begin to venture beyond the rigid limits they have themselves imposed to their work in the past, the discipline of soil science will flourish far beyond its status 30 or 40 years ago, in the heyday of its "agricultural" era.

References

Baveye, P., A.R. Jacobson, S.E.Allaire, J. Tandarich, and R. Bryant, 2006. Whither goes soil science in the US and Canada? Survey results and analysis. Soil Science (in press).

Marbut, C.F. 1921. The contribution of soil surveys to soil science. Society for the Promotion of Agricultural Science Proceedings 41:116-142

◆

Managing Africa's agricultural soils: the future of soil science

Mateete Bekunda
Makerere University, Faculty of Agriculture, P.O. Box 7062, Kampala, Uganda. E-mail mateete@agric.mak.ac.ug

The future of soil science in sub-Saharan Africa (hereafter referred to as Africa) depends on the continent's distinct characteristics: its high concentrations of poor farmers using poor ergonomic tools to work soils dominated by low inherent fertility in support of national economies. In general, these factors lead to soil degradation and for Africa, the need for reversing soil fertility depletion has been equated as being analogous to the need for green-revolution type germplasm in Asia four decades ago.

Several technological options that can be applied to reduce or reverse this degradation exist. They include blanket or zone or crop specific fertiliser recommendations, maintenance fertiliser recommendations, use of low cost inorganic materials, restitution of crop residues and prunings, use of manures, deep soil nutrient capture, biomass transfer, use of agro-industrial by products and wastes, and systems based on biological nitrogen fixation (Nandwa and Bekunda, 1998). Why do African farmers not adopt these technologies but continue to exploit the soils unsustainably?

There are no simple or unique answers to this question; there are soil science's own "unfinished" businesses as well as other interlinked factors that lead to the present level of soil exploitation. The "unfinished" businesses involve generation of information and data to strengthen the advances in science and management innovations that have been made over the years. Three examples serve to illustrate this.

First is that soils of Africa vary widely as a function of ecological and geomorphologic attributes, but these have not been mapped at scales that would allow diversity-based interventions. Taxonomic studies defining these soils have been reconnaissance in nature, including the 1:5 000 000 FAO Soil Map of the World that is still the main reference for many countries in Africa. Soil Science must position itself to utilizing advances in landscape science using remote sensing and GIS tools (Shepherd and Walsh, 2006) that enable more rapid construction of diagnostic soil maps at scales that will bring out appreciation of the diversity. At field-scale, however, enterprise systems could be robust so as to be insensitive to micro-diversity.

Second is that nutrient depletion in Africa is considered alarming but there is uncertainty in its magnitude because of the "sheer lack of certain categories of primary data in the tropics" (Smaling et al., 1997) used in tools (e.g. NUTMON) for computing nutrient losses. The tools were also developed for major nutrients N, P&K yet some systems have problems with exchangeable bases and micro nutrients. Soil science has to address these factors that constrain the relevance of the tool in advancing recommendations for soil nutrient management and policy.

Third is that most research results on soils obtained before the early 1990s were from experiments conducted on research stations or at field sites wholly managed by researchers under idealised conditions. This represents an incomplete picture as management and analysis attached to the results did not represent the smallholder farmers' uncertain, risk-prone and resource scarce environment. Soil science must strengthen the shift toward farmer-inclusive participatory as technological solutions can only be adopted if they are flexible to the local environment.

Science-based biophysical solutions have to interlink with farming as a business. Farmers recognise nutrient depletion that is occurring in fields and will correct it when it is affordable and remunerative to do so (Scoones, 2001). In many parts of Africa, it is the low farm income and high costs of farm inputs that cause serious threats to the soils; farmers working with hoes simply cannot afford to fertilise their fields and apply adequate soil conservation practices to restore fertility. The policy environment that governs both the working of markets and the patterns of public investment in agriculture and the environment are critical.

Therefore, the link between science and development is vital: integration with non-soil science disciplines would help formulate more holistic approaches to soil fertility management that are socially and economically acceptable. Only then will soil science have a niche in agricultural production as it will be seen to contribute to a better product and income rather than increased fertility for its sake.

One of the barriers in addressing the issues above is the inadequate research and extension systems to generate knowledge and innovations and diffuse them to the farm population for use in exploiting opportunities of efficient soil management. This limited capacity is a major limitation to African soil science.

The African Crop Science Society brings together agricultural scientists to biennial conferences to discuss and share progress on the science of promoting crop production and food security in the continent. The last one was held in Entebbe, Uganda in December, 2005, and brought together some 327 scientists. Of the 274 papers presented in the conference, only 22 were in the soil science field (representing 8%) and most used test crops as bioassay, reflecting low capacity in basic soil science research. Studies conducted by the International Service for National Agricultural Research (ISNAR) estimate the percentage of soil science specialist researchers from 22 sub-Saharan Africa countries to be between 5 and 10 of about 7000 NARS researchers. Many of these do not have postgraduate qualifications necessary to generate quality research. If soil science must lead in providing solutions to the leading food production constraint in Africa, there has to be a targeted effort at ensuring a critical number of soil science specialists bringing down the client to researcher ratio to allow consistent partnership interactions.

The soil service physical infrastructure in Africa is limited and of varying quality. The equipping and functioning of research laboratories in Africa have tended to depend more on researcher craftsmanship as national contributions to research funds are limited. The situation is not helped by the declining trend in research funding at global level. Limited infrastructure becomes a disincentive to students wishing to pursue careers in soil science in as much as low funding contributes to low functional capacity.

One must recognise that there are costs associated with capacity to meet these challenges and the future of soil science depends on providing evidence that these costs are comparatively less than those of continued widespread soil degradation.

References

Nandwa, S.M. and Bekunda M.A., 1998. Research on nutrient flows and balances in East and Southern Africa: state-of-the-art. Agriculture, Ecosystems and Environment 71: 5-18.

Scoones, I., 2001. Transforming soils: the dynamics of soil fertility management in Africa. pp 1-44. In: I. Scoones (ed.) Dynamics and diversity: Soil Fertility and Farming Livelihoods in Africa. London: Earthscan.

Shepherd, K.A. and Walsh, M.G., 2006. Diffuse reflectance spectroscopy for rapid soil analysis. In: R. Lal (ed.) Encyclopaedia of Soil Science. Taylor and Francis Books, NY.

Smaling E.M.A., Nandwa, S.M. and Janssen, B.H., 1997. Soil fertility in Africa is at stake. pp. 47-62. In: R.J. Buresh, P.A. Sanchez and F. Calhoun (eds.). Replenishing soil fertility in Africa. SSSA Special Publication 51. SSSA and ASA.

♦

The future of soil science

Winfried E.H. Blum
University of Natural Resources and Applied Life Sciences (BOKU), Vienna Peter-Jordan-Str. 82, 1190 Vienna, Austria. E-mail herma.exner@boku.ac.at

The prediction of the future is always hazardous, even when based on an extrapolation from the past. Nevertheless, an attempt will be made to predict the future of soil science under three different views: 1). Soil science and society; 2). Soil science in relation to other sciences; and 3). Soil science as a science by itself.

Soil science and society

Soil is delivering goods and services to humans and the environment, such as biomass for food, fodder and renewable energy, filtering, buffering and transformation for clean ground water and clean air, besides carbon sequestration and the maintenance of a large variety of organisms, guaranteeing biodiversity. In contrast, soil may be harmful when emitting trace gases to the atmosphere, thus contributing to climate change, or by transport of soil solids to open water surfaces and to air by water and wind erosion, influencing human health by ingestion, inhalation, and skin contact. Finally, soil is protecting archaeological and palaeontological remnants and not only a geogenic but also a cultural heritage.

In the future, two main trends will remain: In countries with food deficiency, soil science will mainly target soil fertility in its largest sense, as long as these deficits exist. Unfortunately, this threat is increasing in many countries in Africa, Asia and South and Central America. In contrast, in countries with sufficient food supply, soil science will increasingly target environmental and cultural issues, such as protection of the food chain against contamination, protection of ground water resources, protection of the air and of human health as well as protection of soil as a cultural and natural heritage, because clean food, clean water and a clean air are the basis of a healthy environment, guaranteeing a long life expectancy of people. Besides these two main trends, in industrial countries, other aspects will gain importance, such as soil science for archaeological dating, forensic soil science, and other applications of soil science to very specific social and economic demands.

In the next 20-30 years, it is not expected that these general features will change very much, because human societies will not much increase their understanding of soil functions and therefore will not expect important contributions from soil science to human societies and the environment, except after dramatic events, such as extreme flooding, large scale pollution or other accidents, but without long lasting effects.

Soil science in relation to other sciences

Soil science developed more than a century ago, from agro-chemistry and agro-geology and is still seen by a broad public as a supporting science for biomass production, especially in agriculture and forestry. However, through the development of new research concepts and the use of specific analytical equipment developed by other sciences, mainly basic physics physico-chemistry, and biochemistry, soil science has developed into very specific areas dealing with all aspects of the weathering crust above rock material, at different scales, from the macro-scale, e.g. regional soil mapping and soil taxonomy, to very small soil particles and their reactions at nano-scale. Therefore, soil science has split up into different special areas, with a danger of losing track of the holistic view of soils.

In contrast to this, through the development in geological sciences in the last two decades, geology is increasingly competing with soil science, e.g. in the field of environmental geology and just recently under the term of agro-geology, an expression which had been abandoned when soil science became a field of science of its own, more than a century ago. Therefore, soil science will increasingly compete with geology, and most probably also with other sciences, especially biological, ecological and computation sciences, and will only be able to maintain itself by intensive co-operation with these sciences, showing that soil science is able to contribute to the understanding of the functioning of terrestrial and aquatic ecosystems.

Soil science as a science by itself

As soil science is targeting not only mineralogical, physical, chemical (especially physico-chemical) soil components and related processes, but also biological ones, it is difficult to understand soil science as one basic science, in contrast to chemistry, physics, and others, disregarding the fact that these have also been split up into a number of very specific scientific domains.

Soil science as a science will probably within 10-20 years increasingly lose its holistic view on soils, because of increasing specialisation, where only specific aspects or particles of soil are investigated thoroughly, down to nano-scales, e.g. in molecular modelling, losing track of the overall functions of soil for humans and the environment. Soil science therefore might probably have problems to maintain itself in the area of other natural sciences, e.g. when these ask what the specific target of soil science is. For example, soil science still has to explain why there are several different soil classification systems, but no general agreement on soil taxonomy on a world-wide level, e.g. about the definition of a soil type or sub-type. This means that soil science cannot define its own research object at a global or regional level. Many soil scientists, or those who call themselves soil scientists, have no general knowledge of soil and its functions any more, but are very specialised, focussing on distinct soil characteristics and processes.

The future development of these specialised areas within soil science will depend to a great extent on other sciences, with regard to analytical concepts and operational tools, which are developed by sciences such as physics and physical chemistry. It can only be hoped that even considering the high degree of specialisation in soil science, soil itself, as a three-dimensional body of the earth's crust, will remain a target by itself and will be understood in its processes and functions, also in the future.

◆

Future of soil science

Ole K. Borggaard
Royal Veterinary and Agricultural University Thorvaldsensvej 40, DK-1871 Frederiksberg, Denmark. E-mail Ole.K.Borggaard@kemi.kvl.dk

Sustainable but markedly improved soil use in a broad global perspective will be an important challenge for future soil science. Research activities should be concentrated on finding ways that clearly and unambiguously can delineate potentials and limitations of different soils in relation to various uses such as plant growth, air and water protection, biodiversity maintenance and preservation of cultural and natural history. Precise measures for soil vulnerability must be created and efficient methods for remediation of degraded soils must be worked out. Equally important, all these research achievements must be communicated clearly and efficiently to planners and practitioners in order to ensure they are implemented and used for the benefit of soil users as well as the entire society. Soil scientist should be encouraged to disseminate research results to practitioners ('ordinary people') and not only to their scientific colleagues. To ensure balanced views and optimum dissemination soil scientists should be prepared to cooperate with other specialists such as economists, anthropologist and communication experts. However, to avoid misinterpretation, confusion and loss of creditability, the communicated information must be clear and correct. More specifically the following, partly overlapping areas can be suggested as priority tasks for future soil science. Some of these activities are already initiated but need to be strengthened and/or focused.

Increased biomass production
In order to improve life conditions in developing countries in South-Saharan Africa more efficient methods are needed to increase and maintain productivity of many, often multi-constraint soils suffering from lack of a range of nutrients, erratic rainfall, pests etc. Due to severe shortage of money, the solutions must be inexpensive and, as far as possible, based on local resources. Knowledge about sensitivity and resilience of many tropical soils, often very different from temperate region soils, is still scarce and should be improved.

Site specific soil use
Soil use should be refined and tuned with focus on production of high quality and unique (high-value) goods, e.g. particularly healthy vegetables, improved livestock feed and wood with special properties. This may be considered an extension of what has been used in wine production for many

years, where wine taste is related to soil type. However, the proposed research on soil-crop interplay should be much better tuned than the current soil-wine interrelation and the achieved quality improvement must be measurable, i.e. based on objective criteria.

Soil reclamation and remediation

Improved methods are needed to reclaim soils that are degraded because of erosion, salinization or because of contaminated with organic and inorganic pollutants. Better on-site and off-site methods and strategies should be developed and optimized for cleaning soils polluted by heavy metals and organic xenobiotica. Remediation strategies for soils saturated with N and P because of excess fertilization for many years also need further attention. At the same time, increased efforts should be put in disseminating existing and new knowledge about these issues to prevent spreading of soil degradation and to reclaim degraded soils.

Natural biotoxins

As a protection against bacteria, insects, animals and other living organisms many plants produce toxins ('natural pesticides') that can be highly toxic, carcinogenic or possess other adverse effects. Knowledge about the behaviour (binding, mobility, persistence) in soils of these compounds is very scarce and should be improved in order to find ways to protect water and food quality. Even more uncertain but equally important is knowledge about the soil behaviour of degradation products (metabolites) of these natural toxins and of many synthetic pesticides. In fact, by focusing on effects rather than origin, future research may put pressure on the current very marked (arbitrary) distinction between natural toxins and xenobiotica such as pesticides.

Land use changes

More focus should be put on afforestation, reestablishment of wetlands, transformation of conventional to ecological agriculture and other kinds of land use changes in order to improve knowledge about such alterations and to avoid adverse effects on the ecosystems, e.g. air and water pollution. Establishment of new plant communities in response to the land use changes may introduce natural toxins to ecosystems that are not adapted ('used') to these toxins, which may therefore be regarded as xenobiotica. For example, Bracken fern, which spreads aggressively on many set-aside farmland soils in Denmark and other countries, produces high amounts of the carcinogenic ptaquiloside that may pose a threat to ground and drinking water quality, because ptaquiloside is rather persistent and mobile in soils. Furthermore, introduction of genetically modified crops may result in release of toxins with unknown behaviour and effects on the soil ecosystem.

Soil-plant interactions

Mutual interactions between soils and plants are 'common wisdom' but the precise mechanisms are only partly understood. Knowledge about the precise requirements to the soil of many plants, e.g. various tree species is lacking. Such information is important to ensure ecosystem stability especially where the land use is changed.

Soil quality concept

Launching of the soil quality concept more than a decade ago definitely placed focus on soils. However, the multi-functionality of the concept has proven difficult to handle. Thus, an intensively fertilized soil has high quality as medium for plant growth but low quality in other functions, e.g. groundwater protection against nitrate pollution. Furthermore, the concept is based on criteria, some of which are contextual and subjective. The challenge is to develop the concept so it can integrate and operationally recognize the simultaneity of the diverse and often conflicting soil functions. If this proves impossible, the soil science community must redefine soil quality in terms of scientifically sound and objective criteria.

In addition

Much is still to be learnt about soils such as soil components (minerals, organic matter, soil solution and soil air), soil processes (acidification, humification, clay migration, podzolization, weathering etc.), carbon and nitrogen sequestration and transport of water and solute in various soils. Transport of organic and inorganic colloids and their role as pollutant carriers are subjects of current research which must be strengthened. Soil classification should also be improved in order to address simplicity and user-friendliness but also to enable it to cope with anthropogenic effects in a more straightforward way.

◆

Future of soil science

Johan Bouma

Spoorbaanweg 35, 3911 CA Rhenen, the Netherlands. E-mail Johan.bouma@planet.nl

As in any science, the future of soil science will depend on what we, soil scientists, will do or will fail to do. Even though I am optimistic by nature, I am not encouraged with what I see currently happening in soil science research. There is much fragmented and self-centred subdisciplinary work ("atomization") on e.g. soil physics, - chemistry, – biology and spatial statistics. I am not questioning the scientific quality nor relevance of that work but I feel that the pieces don't fit together anymore. They should if we want to be recognized as a full fledged partner in large, interdisciplinary projects on land use, climate change and water use, to just mention three major international research efforts in which soil science could play a key role but does not. The International Council of Science (ICSU) is clear: its vision points to a world "where science is used for the benefit of all…and where scientific knowledge is effectively linked to policy making". Its goal is to: "strengthen international science for the benefit of society" and it coordinates several large interdisciplinary, international programs, in which we could be more involved. Such types of interdisciplinary policy-oriented projects are also increasingly initiated by international, national and regional research organisations.

Some problems

Much of our published work appears to be rather self- centred and reference to the policy arena and to interactive processes is seen by many soil scientists as unscientific and compromising. Our actions to fit the ICSU ambitions and those of comparable other funding and policy agencies are inadequate in my view. Some arbitrarily selected indications:

1. We still cannot define soil quality, which is an essential element of environmental regulations, while the quality of air and water is well defined. This implies that the soil message cannot be communicated as effectively as we might desire.

2. A leading scientist recently concluded that widely used soil erosion models essentially yield empirical results because of lack of good basic soil data (Stroosnijder, 2005). This challenges our scientific pretensions.

3. Manure regulations in Europe to protect water quality largely ignore soil expertise and focus on farm management aspects, while in effect soil processes govern water quality and should be the basis for such regulations.

4. Engineers, biologists and geographers mine our extensive databases and use pedotransferfunctions to feed their comprehensive simulation models, often without our involvement.

5. Prominent simulation models for crop growth have very detailed submodules for plant physiology but a very simple soil component, such as the tipping bucket approach. This creates unbalanced models that do not adequately reflect our soil expertise. This is also true for other comprehensive environmental models with rudimentary soil submodels.

Opportunities

We seem to have lost our roots, anchored in the nineteenth century, defining soils as living, natural bodies in a landscape as a basis for defining dynamic and interrelated soil physical, chemical and biological processes. Soil classification focuses on natural soils (genoforms) and this is a limitation when studying land use. However, soil survey can be extended to effects of soil management on any given soil series by distinguishing phenoforms (Bouma, 2005). What are our opportunities in future and how can we rise to the occasion? Elsewhere, I suggested some drastic changes in the way we do our research (Bouma, 2005) and I will not repeat that here. I suggest we focus here on specific future opportunities which are abundantly present:

1. In Europe we see new opportunities in environmental legislation, most recently the comprehensive water guideline, which is focussed on watersheds. Defining 3D fluxes of water and chemicals in a landscape and watershed context is a logical start of defining soil processes, combining soil- and hydrological expertise in the new discipline of hydropedology (Lin et al, 2006).

2. Similarly, in the Netherlands spatial planning is based on the "three-layer model" starting with conditions of geology, soil and water and associated ecological conditions in the first layer, followed by transportation infrastructure in the second and settlements in the third. Developing the first layer should be major activity for soil scientists.

3. The just approved new soil framework for the European Union offers many opportunities for soil science and is based on the *Pressure, State, Response* principle, reflecting societal processes and the manner in which they can be affected by soil management. This, again, offers excellent opportunities for soil science.

How to rise to the challenge?

I suggest five approaches: (i) Combat "atomization" by starting projects with an integrated analysis of soil processes in a landscape context, which still leaves room for cutting-edge disciplinarity in the end; (ii) Facilitate linking up with interdisciplinary projects by defining our expertise at different knowledge ("K") levels, ranging from tacit and descriptive to cutting-edge quantitative (Bouma, 2001). Bouma and Droogers (1999) illustrated this for the soil moisture supply capacity; (iii) Extend the reach of soil survey by not only considering genoforms but also phenoforms of given soil series, reflecting effects of different types of management; (iv) Combat database addiction and initiate extensive field monitoring using a wide array of new, modern sensing techniques, (v) Improve communication with colleagues, policy makers and stakeholders by joining the information revolution.

References

Bouma, J., 2001. The new role of soil science in a network society. Soil Science 166: 874-879.

Bouma, J., 2005. Soil scientists in a changing world. Advances in Agronomy 88: 67-96.

Bouma, J. and Droogers, P., 1999. Comparing different methods for estimating the soil moisture supply capacity of a soil series subjected to different types of management. Geoderma 92: 185-197.

ICSU (International Council of Science), 2005. Strategic Plan for 2006-2012. www.icsu.org.

Lin, H., Bouma, J., Pachepsky, Y., Western, A., Thompson, J., van Genuchten, R., Vogel, H.J. and Lilly, A., 2006. Hydropedology: Synergistic integration of pedology and hydrology. Water Resources Research (in press).

Stroosnijder, L., 2005. Measurement of erosion: is it possible? Catena 64: 162-174.

♦

The future of soil science in industrial societies

Henrik Breuning-Madsen

University of Copenhagen, Institute of Geography, Øster Voldgade 10, DK-1350, Denmark. E-mail hbm@geogr.ku.dk

Soil science based on pedology, founded by Dokuchaev, is less than 100 years old. Since then his concepts have defined soil science and most national soil surveys have adopted pedology as a main descriptor in soil mapping. Until recently, the major task for soil survey organisations has been to produce regional and point based information for agricultural production or forestry. This has been done at national levels using nationally developed soil classification and soil profile description systems, supported by analytical methods to characterize soils.

During the last decades, the focus of soil science in the industrial world has changed significantly because the focus of societies has changed from agricultural production and forestry towards environmental issues. Many of these problems can still be solved at national levels but some have to be solved internationally, which entails merging soil information from different countries. Furthermore, many environmental problems are so complex that they can not be solved by soil scientists alone but require cooperation with other scientists such as biologists, chemists and specialists in computer modelling. This development makes it necessary for soil scientists to change the focus of their research from themes concerned with increasing agricultural and forestry production towards environmental impact assessments and how to solve environmental problems such as the contamination of soil, erosion, carbon sequestration and nutrient leaching.

Most environmental problems are complex and need detailed laboratory analyses, the development of new analytical methods and plot experiments at different scales in relation to time and space. Another important issue is the upscaling of point based results to regional scales, for example, within catchments or administrative areas. This development raises several questions on how to obtain the most suitable soil maps for interpolation, how to extrapolate results obtained by modelling point data, what basic soil analytical data should be available for modelling, and how can we educate soil scientists so they have a basic understanding of the transformations needed to convert soil data into derived thematic maps that can be used by municipal, county, country or international administrations. Some environmental problems such as leaching of nutrients to the sea or contamination by air born contaminants do not obey 'political' borders.

National computerized soil maps might serve as the tool for upscaling point measurements to a regional scale, but they might not always have the necessary information and might have to be updated by attributes. Because the national soil maps have not been developed according to a single common international methodology and classification system it is necessary when operating at an international scale to develop an international system and to unify the national systems. WRB is the global soil classification system but it is questionable how well-suited it is for upscaling of modelled point based information. The morpho-genetic approach does not functioning well in heavily manipulated soils that are ploughed, limed, manured and drained. The soil chemistry and physics of these soils do not necessary reflect the initial pedological processes that formed the soils and hereby the WRB-name. Some profile features might be relicts such as gley in drained soils, while others, such as mollic/umbric epepidons do not give any meaning in ploughed or limed areas. Information provided from the names might be misleading, irrelevant or carrying a low level of information. Another problem is that WRB, to some degree, is based on properties that are difficult to measure and scientists describing and classifying the same profile might not arrive at the same result. This shows that new thinking is needed on how to make international soil maps at various scales that fits today's purposes.

In order to be able to run regional environmental modelling, nationwide or international soil profile and analytical databases must be established. National databases exist for some countries but they are not established in relation to any international common standards. Thus, regional models are problematic in some countries due to missing data, while when modelling across borders databases have to be created to match the international soil maps. To comply with this issue, we have to set up standards for analytical methodologies so that cross-country comparisons of data become possible. Furthermore, soil scientists must be willing to estimate missing data in their databases, because if a model needs data that are missing additional information must be created data based on knowledge rules. In that case it would be the best if the soil expert makes this estimation. Soil scientists should agree on what data to store in a database. Previously, the focus was mainly on chemical data and, for example, soil physical data like soil water retention data are sparse despite their importance in regional water models.

Politically, there is an increasing understanding of soil as a limited and vulnerable resource, like water and air. Therefore, discussions on how to protect soil and to follow the state of art for soil are ongoing and soil scientists have a role to play in the building of monitoring grids or monitoring catchment areas, how to collect and analyze soil samples and derive conclusions on the state of art.

Finally, soil scientist must work on introducing remote sensing techniques that range from satellite born sensors to ground-based instruments that include terrain-penetrating radar, geo-electric equipment or magnetometers. Remote sensing in precision farming is well-used. Applying inorganic fertilisers according to soil maps and the precise location of the tractor using GPS are common. Soil maps made by combining traditional soil surveys and remotely sensed data make it possible to indicate the degree of precision and statistical errors developed from geo-statistic evaluations. That is important information when characterizing and expressing the local or overall accuracy of the soil maps.

In conclusion, soil science plays an important role in detecting and solving environmental problems at regional scales. In order to do so, we have to change our focus from agricultural production towards environmental issues.

◆

Soil environment, soil use and socio-economic implications

Wolfgang Burghardt
Dept. of Soil Technology, Faculty of Bio- and Geosciences, University Duisburg - Essen, 45117 Essen, Germany. E-mail wolfgang.burghardt@uni-essen.de

To my understanding, from personal and more practical experience with soils, the importance of soil science will be related to three viewpoints in the future: (1) the focus on soils as carrier of properties and as a product of environment and its rapid change; (2) the role of land use; (3) linkage of soil science with socio-economics.

Soils and the environment

There is a split in soil science between prior orientation on soil properties and soil development based on processes. The main focus of recent definitions of soils refers to soil and surface layers properties. Furthermore this reductionist view on soils is focused on material properties and on plant production. Following this trend, soil science becomes a science of soil segments and not of soils. This corresponds with industrial-technical development which focuses on a limited number of economically promising products.

Many essential products and functions provided by soils can be generated without soils. Technical protein production in aqua culture is such an example. Clean drinking water can be also provided by technical measures instead using soils for protection of groundwater against pollution. The idea of dealing with soils as material is that material quality can be standardised. So soil quality can be certified. But is this really an appropriate concept to consider? I learned from my visit of sherry distilleries in Jerez, Spain, that the soil of lowest quality, a soil from white marl, is the best for sherry wine. Demands to soils are too different that there could be an unique and universal soil quality concept as there is for construction materials for example.

Immediately after the deposition of a natural or man-made soil, the environment starts its action by chemical, physical, mechanical and biological processes. Soil development is always a natural process. With time the properties of the deposited material soils acquire a second and third group of properties. The second group is created by the kind of combination, diversity, duration and stage of actions of elements of environment. They determine new properties of the surface layers which are defined as soils, consisting of horizons and a spatial pattern of diverse properties.

At the one hand soil horizons and at the other soil pattern in landscapes are like a sequence of reactors governing processes. Soil properties obtain their tangible assets as a result of various processes. The high dynamics of destruction, replacement and sealing of soils results in new processes, for example, such for human life fundamental ones as CO_2 accumulation in the topsoil free of humus, change of evapo-transpiration and groundwater renewal.

Development of new compounds and organisms, and dispersal of both all over the world is risky. Soils with highly diverse properties have a higher capacity to buffer and to resist adverse effects for a longer time. Such soils give us the chance to detect potential future catastrophe, and to reduce risks. "Waldsterben" (forest dieback) illustrates this.

The third group of soil properties is that soils are always unique, however close to other soil individuals. Beside the genetic pool and the lithosphere, soil is one of the world biggest carrier of information. The right and ability of individuality and to have relatives and their importance in human life brings up the question of the effects on human development when information from dead and living nature are destroyed and lost.

In my opinion, guidance along procedural concepts based on the actions of the environment will increase the opportunity for soil scientists to contribute to sustainable human life and to public promotion of soil science.

Soils and land use

Most soils are changed by humans which have become the largest environmental factor influencing soils and their processes. In cities soils have a totally new environment. This can happen by particular use of a plot of land and by material and heat emissions from use of other plots. There is a third component of dependence. In a commercial world, plots of different areas are related by material and energy import and export. The relationship of soils becomes a result of different steps of production and commerce on several sites and not longer of gravity forces and gradients of material and energy concentration within a landscape. For many areas, soils and their relationships and spatial sequences of occurrence and properties will be determined by the economic relationships of plots. New relationships of soils are not restricted to a landscape but can exist over all continents. In the future with an advanced economy, the extent of anthropogenic soils will increase drastically. Soil science will continue to be important when its focus is on soil use as main future factor of soil environment, soil development, soil properties and soil functions.

Soils and socio-economics

Today, socio-economic costs determine policy in most countries. The role of soils in this context has not been clearly defined until now. One main problem will be the divergent interests between private and public enterprises including governments' interest in short-term return on investments, tax and ownership, and public provision which needs long-term sustainability of social and economic living conditions.

Social expenses are large in many governmental budgets. They are necessary to support poor, ill and old people, and families. Expenses for an environmental policy which supports health, food and other natural products, recreation, and climate regulation reduces social costs and gain social stability. Soils have considerable potentials in this context.

The problem is that soil science is embodied in environmental science and agronomy. This means it is embodied in the wrong administrations; these are not the institutions for balancing financial future benefits of soils and costs of soil protection measures today or which are already hit by economic and social disasters of climate change.

The huge importance of transport and import of material and energy into soils by socio-economic processes must gain a main focus of soil science on research of material mass and energy balances, both locally and globally. Important contributions from soils are:

- production of food, fuel, raw material, new chemical compounds (for example for plastics), and their residues in soils;
- clean water supply for agriculture and for rapid growing urban populations;
- health, dilution and transformation of noxious compounds from emissions and occurrence of pathogenic organisms in soils;
- atmospheric CO_2 reduction the increase of plant mass production and of plant residues incorporation into soils;
- change of albedo and for the heat storage capacity of soils;
- capacities of new soils as habitats and reservoir for particular organisms of interest for economy;
- use of soils in sealed areas for example for storm water infiltration, and for street trees and plants in sealed areas.

Soil scientists have to learn that their work is much more related to socio-economics than to environmental administration. Soil science is contributing to short-term return of investments and taxes, but in particular to avoidance of long-term costs. This includes highly increased costs of health and other risk provision and insurances, and also of large long-term investments such as for fuel and water. The future of soil science depends on co-operation with socio-economic factors.

◆

The future of soil science: view from a developing country

Kep Coughlan

Hassall and Associates, Canberra, Australia. E-mail *cardiap_atl@online.com.kh until August 2006; afterwards kepcoughlan@optusnet.com.au*

My view is not as an academic or as a practicing researcher in soil science, but rather as a person with a perspective of soil and land related needs (and the future of these needs) which is strongly coloured by my environment. I work in Cambodia, one of the poorest countries in south-east Asia, where attitudes are determined by the strong poverty alleviation objectives which must operate in an environment of imperfect Governance, lack of integrated planning, and in some cases the use of international donor funds to set the development agenda. Problems viewed from a developing country perspective are often magnified or distorted compared with the view from a developed country. These changes in perspective often allow you to see familiar problems in a new light. I will illustrate these differences with reference to three familiar issues for soil scientists:

The need for land resource planning

In most developing countries there are examples where activities such as forest clearing are carried out for private benefit. This may occur partly through lack of national planning, and also because of a lack of realization that the collective costs of such activities far outweigh the individual benefits. Good bio-physical and socio-economic data can make a real contribution to limiting environmental degradation during a country's developmental phase. However, the data are rarely available, and when it is information is in different forms and at different scales, so that use for planning is difficult or impossible. The contribution that good planning can make in a developing country is significantly magnified compared with a developed country because the environmental damage at scales ranging from local to global *is* much higher.

There are also the possibilities of saving unique eco-systems through appropriate planning intervention. The *Tonle* Sap Lake in North West Cambodia is a world famous environmental phenomenon where vast areas of forest are flooded in the wet season producing a fecund fish breeding resource. However, there is competition for use of these areas by poor farmers who clear the forests on state land to grow rice as the flood waters recede. Short term economic gains are made, but the potential damage to fish resources, a staple source of protein for Cambodians, is enormous. Good land resource planning, and intensification of rice production in other

31

areas, is the obvious solution, but one which may be lost during rapid development.

Land treatment of wastes

The use of soil as a bio-filter is an important option for environmental management in developed countries. In developing countries sewage and industrial wastes are often discharged into water bodies with resulting environmental and health consequences. Since soils are often infertile, use of acceptable liquid wastes for irrigation of industrial crops would have the double advantage of increasing productivity and reducing environmental damage. Just when the nutrients from sewage are so badly needed to maintain soil fertility they are often flushed down the river. Techniques for land treatment of wastes are available in developed countries, and application of these in developing countries is a huge opportunity.

Organic farming

All traditional farming systems were organic. Now some, such as "slash and burn" are being criticized because of environmental implications and unsustainability associated with the shortening of forest regeneration phases. Organic products are a niche market, and therefore organic farming has its place. International donors in Cambodia are arguing that since local farmers have not traditionally used chemical fertilizers and pesticides, they have a comparative advantage in the export market to supply organic products to developed countries. While this is true at a limited scale, the question must be asked: "Is the application of organic farming practices at a national level sustainable"? If not, Cambodian farmers could be denied the benefits of improved productivity and profitability in the name of providing products preferred by customers, particularly in developed countries. At the same time, valuable resources would be diverted from building conventional markets within the region.

I am sceptical that a farmer can farm organically from material produced from his or her own land. Contentious issues such as this must be faced, but in developing countries there is limited scientific expertise, and the agenda is often determined by foreign experts. There is a need for logical debate based on empirical evidence, but this is lacking. For example, one group of protagonists for organic farming in Cambodia was heard to state "If you apply chemicals to your fields your children will be born deformed". This emotive statement of course puts urea in the same basket as "Agent Orange". This is an area where soil scientists can make a real contribution by quantifying nutrient balances, the potential for nutrient recycling through plants, and biological sources of nutrients such as nitrogen fixation.

Global studies show that many developed countries are accumulating nutrients through import of agricultural produce, whereas nutrients in some developing countries are being depleted. If it turns out that organic farming practices are not sustainable at any reasonable level of production at a farm scale, should soil scientists be lobbying for the subsidization of chemical fertilizers (setting a common world price) rather than sentencing developing countries to continued low yield? At a recent conference I was told that urea cost US$90 in Europe yet US$700 in Malawi, where the farmers can least afford it.

Developing countries will always be laboratories in which the "good ideas" of scientists from developed countries are tested. This of course is positive, except when strategies that may work well in some situations are applied to all situations by enthusiastic supporters. One such good idea is the system for rice intensification which proposes, *inter alia*, that rice is a normal cereal that is adapted to growing in ponds, but which will perform much better in drained conditions with no water stress. Supporters state: "Rice plants are being flooded, crowded and poisoned (with chemical fertilizers)". This system needs to be rigorously tested since there are serious adverse consequences for poor farmers if the theories are wrong.

In conclusion, the future of soil science in developing countries is not all "science", but good science and empirical evidence is important to allow rational debate. We must reclaim the right to, and be involved in, debate in areas such as organic farming (in soil science) and issues such as GMO at a wider agricultural scale.

My advice to soil scientists is to become involved in research and development in developing countries. Not only will this bring real benefits to the countries involved, but it will provide different perspectives which often clarify insular (geographic or disciplinary) points of view.

◆

Future of soil science: a vision from Europe

Endre Dobos
Dept. of Physical Geography and Environmental Sciences, University of Miskolc, 3515 Miskolc-Egyetemváros, Hungary. E-mail ecodobos@uni-miskolc.hu

At the beginning of the new millennium problems of land degradation, disparity of production potentials and of population carrying capacities became obvious international concerns. Globalization and global environmental issues necessitate the collection and interpretation of global, harmonized soil information. It is a great challenge and task for future soil scientist to provide appropriate soils data to the society in an info-centric world.

Thematic science, like soil science, as a stand alone scientific discipline, cannot subsist without integrating itself into a goal and problem oriented society. It means that knowledge represented by the soil science community has to be understandable and marketable for other scientific fields, and the data used by the interdisciplinary models has to answer the needs of the models.

Soil data are required for numerous applications run by non-soil scientist and sometimes used without full understanding its meaning, origin, quality and its usability and limitations. A communication language is needed to transfer the knowledge between soil data providers and the "non-soil users" of the data. The task is broad and includes the development of harmonized methodology and language for different scale of soil descriptions to digital soil and land mapping and information technology.

The author represents the digital soil mapping and the soil classification society from the European Community, where the harmonization of the national databases and the development of spatially and thematically consistent international, cross-border databases are the key issues on the continental and also on the regional level. Integrated management of the natural and human resources over Europe is a beneficial outcome and potential of the European integration. In this context I would like to highlight some of the major issues and driving forces of soil science in the near future.

Soil database development

Soil data of various scales, detail and accuracy have been collected all over the world in the last one and a half century. Soil survey was the major factor in the development of our soil science knowledge, it helped understanding and classifying soils and their function in the landscape. Many of the best soil scientists earned their knowledge through soil surveys. However, many soil survey campaigns are over and the knowledge represented and maintained by the soil-surveyor community is slowly fading away. We need soil surveys (i) to take over the heritage from the old surveyors; (ii) to update the knowledge represented by the soil maps and databases; and (iii) to transfer this information into the content and format required by the data user society.

The world has changed and the priorities have been shifted from agricultural production towards environmental issues, especially in the more developed, industrialized part of the world. Available soil data often fails to provide answers needed to manage our environmental resources. New kind of soil data are needed to complement existing databases and it has to be integrated into a GIS to provide spatial detail required by the users. Digital soil mapping techniques, as additional tools for spatializing the soil variability and diversity is integrated into traditional toolset of soil mapping. The ratio of quantitative versus qualitative procedures will increase providing an improved spatial and thematic consistency of the data, recordability of the procedures and measures of data accuracy. Metadata, quality assurance and quality measures will be a crucial part of all databases, especially when data is used outside soil science.

Harmonization

Many environmental issues cross political borders. Data, which has been collected on the national level using national standards, has to be used alongside to extract information needed to solve environmental problems. This task is difficult due to differences between the national systems. Spatial inconsistency is most evident and a problem that can be recognized easily through non-matching polygons along the political border. A less visible and thus greater problem is the thematic inconsistency which comes through the different understanding and interpretation of the reference system by the data providers and "translators". The initiation of a new, harmonized field survey campaign seems unrealistic in the near future. The only solution is the harmonization of existing data, which is being done within the European Community. Harmonization requires a common system and classification of soil variables. It should not be more than a simple interface, where all national data sources can "plug in" the processed, translated data window in the required format and contents. These standards are missing for most of the soil variables. One important task of soil science is the development of these standardized data frameworks. The World Reference Base is the best example for this.

Soil Classification

Most soil classification systems were started in the middle of the last century and began to be used since the 1960s based on genetic principles. Modifications were made in many systems. Based on experiences and the expanded knowledge emphasis shifted from the genetic approach, to the use of quantifiable soil properties as differentiating criteria. This diagnostic approach with parametric definitions feeds better the digital data bases and serves the harmonization efforts. The official correlation classification system is the World Reference Base (WRB) for Soil Resources. The use of such correlation system ensures common characterization, identification and interpretation of soil units and helps the development of cross boundary soil databases. Many national systems have adapted the diagnostic approach, taking over the specifications of the diagnostic criteria, horizons and properties of the WRB, while keeping the national nomenclature and classification. This approach makes correlation between the national systems easy, while maintain the local detail and traditions of the national systems.

Pedometrics

Quantitative soil science, so-called pedometrics, is a relative recent development in soil science. It covers a great portion from digital soil mapping techniques to modelling of soil processes and variables. Until recently, our understanding of soil processes was organized by a set of qualitative rules, which we believe to be true and explains the nature and properties of soils in a given environment. Pedometricians try to quantify these rules and relationships to test the rules themselves, to explain the spatial and temporal variability and changes of soil properties and to forecast trends of the future. These trials make use of the most advanced quantitative techniques and digital data sources to test what we believe to be true. The results are stimulating! It can prove that we are on the right track, and can prove the opposite as well. But the most important message is that our understanding and knowledge is still far behind the reality. The good thing is that we still have a lot to do and can enjoy the work we like, doing research in soil science to better understand soils!

◆

Soil science, global environments and human wellbeing

Julian Dumanski

16 Burnbank St., Ottawa, Canada. E-mail jdumanski@rogers.com

> *Environmental problems resulting from human activities have begun to threaten the sustainability of earth's life support system. Among the most critical challenges facing humanity are the conservation, restoration, and wise management of the earth's resources.*
>
> Lubchenko, 1998

The study of the soil as a natural body began as an agricultural science, but its future lies with the environmental sciences. Soil is a living body, it is an integral part of the earth's terrestrial ecosystems, and an important component in providing global environmental services and benefits. Human over-exploitation of natural resources has resulted in considerable degradation of global ecosystems (natural capital), and recent estimates are that this degradation will continue as a consequence of a likely three to six-fold increase in global GDP by 2050, even while global populations are expected to level off (UNEP, 2005). The challenge for soil scientists is to integrate and deepen their science, in consort with environmental, social, economic and political professionals, to help resolve these major global environmental problems.

The state of the environment

Currently, about 25% of the terrestrial earth's surface is intensively managed, either in agriculture, managed natural and plantation forests, or managed nature preserves (UNEP, 2005), and about 70% of the total land surface is under some form of human intervention (Vitousek 1994). Evidence on how this degree of land use change is impacting on global ecosystems and human wellbeing is illustrated by the UNEP Millennium Ecosystems Assessment Report (UNEP, 2005):

- More land was converted to cropland in the last 50 years than in 150 years between 1700 – 1850;
- Fresh water withdrawals doubled (70% for agriculture), and water impoundments behind dams quadrupled;
- Flows of biologically available nitrogen doubled, and flows of phosphorus tripled. Almost half of all synthetic fertilizers have been used since 1985;
- Atmospheric concentration of CO_2 has increased by 32 % since 1750, with approximately 60% of this since 1959;

- Human activities have resulted in significant losses of wildlife habitat and global biodiversity.

Degradation of ecosystem services represent a lose of capital assets, and while this can sometimes be justified to produce greater gains in other services, often more degradation of ecosystem services takes place than is in the best interest of society (UNEP, 2005).

International conventions

The international environmental conventions provide a platform and a focus for reversing the degradation of soil on a global scale. While all of the conventions deal with complex issues of land management at global and national levels, it is only the United Nations Convention to Combat Desertification, the United Nations Framework Convention on Climate Change, and its subsidiary, the Kyoto Protocol, and the United Nations Forum on Forests which specifically refer to land degradation and soil management. Other related conventions include the United Nations Convention on Biological Diversity, the framework agreements on international waters, and the Ramsar treaty on wetlands. The international conventions do not guide activities in soil conservation, but they provide the fora and global agenda for soil issues to be integrated more comprehensively into the global environmental agenda.

Soil science and ecosystem management

The global terrestrial environment consists of a mosaic of ecologically linked, natural and human land use ecosystems. The health of these ecosystems, defined as ecosystem integrity, depends on the ecosystem components and the synergy of processes that pass between them and promote a steady flow of production and environmental goods and services (GEF, 2004). Land degradation affects selected ecosystem components and functional cycles, thereby impairing the synergy and the security of services that flow therefrom. The role of soil science in mitigation of land degradation is to focus attention on the linkages and synergy among and across identified components of the local and global ecosystems, realizing that the soil is the centre point and the hub through which all processes must pass.

A landscape approach is required to study the role of soil as an integral component of natural and converted (managed) ecosystems (Dumanski, et al. 2002). Landscape studies promote understanding of ecological and socio-economic interactions, linking local benefits to global environmental goods and services over delineable areas of the earth's terrestrial surface. Agro-ecosystems and other managed ecosystems experience different pressures, energy flows, and dynamics, and these have to be better understood not only in terms of capital return (yield, etc.), but also as a consequence of human interventions on natural systems.

Mitigation of land degradation and ecosystem restoration often requires action on legislative and economic initiatives, such as creating an enabling policy environment, greater use of economic instruments such as carbon trading, payment for ecosystem services, certification schemes, etc., incorporation of non-market values in ecosystem investment, as well as removal of perverse subsidies and other policies that impact negatively on ecosystem management. However, the final resolution requires targeted technological innovations in soil science which improve the health of the soil while concurrently providing economic benefits (Dumanski et al., 2002).

Soil scientists are already participating in many of these initiatives, but the evolving soil science will be more encompassing of other sciences and other approaches. To enable this transition, however, soil science will have to move from its puritanical, uni-scientific positions of the past, and become a science which acts to integrate all facets of the biophysical and human environments within which it functions. After all, is this not where one finds the soil in nature?

References

Dumanski, J., P.A. Bindraban, W.W. Pettapiece, P. Bullock, R.J.A. Jones, and A. Thomasson, 2002. Land classification, sustainable land management, and ecosystem health. In: Encyclopedia of food and agricultural sciences. Encyclopedia of life support systems. EOLSS Publishers, Oxford, UK.

GEF, 2004. Scope and Coherence of the land degradation activities of the GEF. GEF/C.24/6. GEF, Washington, D.C.

Lubchenko J., 1998. Entering the century of the environment: A new social contract for science. Science 279: 491- 497.

UNEP, 2005. Millennium Ecosystem Assessment. UNEP. Nairobi, Kenya.

Vitousek, P.M., 1994. Beyond global warming: ecology and global change. Ecology 75: 1861-1876.

♦

Future of soil science

Hari Eswaran

USDA Natural Resources Conservation Service, 1400 Independence Avenue, Washington DC 20250, USA. E-mail hari.eswaran@WDC.usda.gov

Science provides the knowledge base for humans to better manage their environment and thereby ensure a favourable quality of life for present and future generations. The latter notion, has taken on a new sense of urgency. Scientists have debated the limits of the Earth's capacity to support continuing population growth. Some scientists see limits to the capacity of soils to produce the food and fibre needed for the anticipated increases in population. Other scientists think it premature to underestimate the potential of future technologies to vastly increase food production. Today, there are about 800 million people who are undernourished or malnourished and another 2.2 billion people who manage on a minimum caloric intake. There is a strong climatic-geographical correlation to under nourishment. Most of the undernourished live where it is too cold, too dry, too wet or too hot for a high level of agricultural production. Additionally, poverty and unstable markets and governments mean that many of these countries are not in a position to benefit from advances in technology. Poverty, civil strife, and corrupt governments, which are often inextricably linked, create hurdles to expanding the capability to produce and distribute food and feed effectively to address under nourishment.

Soil science, like many other sciences, was in the doldrums during the last decade of the 20th century. The belief that biotechnology would overcome all constraints on agricultural production meant less emphasis on the need to understand soils. The limits, and not just the promises, of biotechnology are clearer now. The future of soil science depends on how well we manage smoother and stable scientific progress. Soil science must retain its identity while demonstrating its value to other sciences; it must contribute to but not be skewed by accomplishments in related sciences. The challenge for soil science is to remain relevant, produce results that are meaningful not just to scientists but to the public, and continue to push new frontiers in the field. The future hinges on how we meet this continuing challenge.

We generally do not excel in demonstrating our contributions and value to the public. In fact, we avoid engaging the public. The 1960s and 1970s were a peak in our profession, rallying the scientific community to work on terminology and classification. We had a defined goal and we worked toward it. Clearly, the soil science society will work and excel when confronted with a challenge. The current leadership must bring forward a new challenge to mobilize the Society's technical strength toward a clear and meaningful objective. The forthcoming IUSS World Congress of Soil Science promises to be a good one, and could be a great one if it brings forward such a spark. Land degradation and desertification has great potential to be such a rallying point, and could be with the support it deserves from the Society.

Our future depends on our ability to engage the public in decisions about the science. To keep the science alive we have to remain relevant and produce results that are meaningful to society. This is done through our social contract. Soil science was strongest when benefiting society was its avowed goal, even when we were overly optimistic about the promise of soil science. We have to encourage and ensure greater dialogue between scientists, policymakers and the general public. We have to be transparent to questions like: Who we are? Why is the science relevant? In what direction are we going and how do we determine that? How does the public benefit?

There are many issues affecting our ability to ensure sustainable agricultural systems, most of which are socioeconomic in nature. Three of most important issues are:

1. *Rapid decline in quality and quantity of global natural resources due to degradation (desertification) and uncontrolled resource consumption in many countries, specifically developing countries, stresses global agriculture with long term negative consequences.*
About 33 percent of the Earth's land surface has potential for desertification. This is about 42 million km^2 and affects more than 1 billion people. By 2020, if appropriate actions are not taken, the numbers of persons affected will more than double. As a major part of the population increase is to take place in Asia and Africa, these regions will suffer the most. With a reduction of the ability of these countries to be self-sufficient in food, food security will emerge as a major global issue forcing the western countries to provide more food. This can stress more land resources including a net drain or imbalances in soil nutrient resources in the donor countries. The situation may be aggravated by climate change.

2. *Absence of current and reliable natural resources global databases reduces the ability of developed nations to address potential famine or socio-political unrest, specifically those arising from lack of or inferior quality land resources.*
There is increasing evidence that civil unrest in many countries leading to major conflicts is strongly related to availability to, and quality of, land resources. Early warning indicators of famine and projections of collapse of ecosystems can help to avert some of these conflicts. Stabilizing the countries' agriculture systems, specifically through the implementation of appropriate soil and water conservation policies, can help reduce the impacts of natural calamities. Drought prone countries, particularly those dependent

upon livestock, can reduce losses by judicious use of grazing lands. Large scale deforestation and burning of forests in the tropics affects climate with additional impacts on air quality.

3. *Absence of a global collaborative mechanism to ensure that soil management standards and quality control procedures in soil survey and resource assessment are available to all. .*
Developing global databases is expensive, but use of accepted international standards and procedures can make development more efficient since domestic databases may be combined into a global system. When different standards are used, the cost of maintaining the database increases exponentially and the ability to share information is reduced.

The desire of all countries should be to adopt policies that support mutual goals of soil health, clean water and sustainable farming. Methods and systems needed to accomplish these are objectives are: an assessment and monitoring program that tracks the quality of the resource conditions, the use of appropriate technologies, and environmental policies that enable the practice of sustainable agriculture. Achieving this situation will enable countries to fulfil their desires. Soil Science can serve as the vehicle to achieve this goal.

♦

Future of soil science

Richard Fowler
ARC-GCI, KwaZulu-Natal, South Africa. E-mail rmfowler@iafrica.com

"The farmers are doing it, the extension workers are trying to stop them and the researchers are trying to understand what's happening!" This summation of the Brazilian Conservation Agriculture revolution at the end of the 20th century applied to many of the innovative crop production systems then in use. Both 'modern' and traditional farmers practising, for example, organic farming, reduced tillage, LEISA (Low External Input Sustainable Agriculture) and SRI (System of Rice Intensification) frequently found themselves at odds with advisers with limited access to recent findings or the insight or information to incorporate 'discipline-blinkered' results into farming systems. Researchers all too often made little attempt to identify felt or real needs, discover or respect indigenous knowledge, understand the effects of proposed interventions on other aspects (physical, chemical, biological, environmental, animal or human) of production systems, ensure appropriate knowledge reached potential users, or understand or influence opinion leaders.

In the global village, areas devoted to crop production continued to shrink as a result, for example, of urbanization, erosion and global warming, increasing the need to cultivate degraded and marginal soils, utilize mulches, reduce tillage, practise Conservation Agriculture (minimum soil disturbance, maximum soil cover and crop rotation) and produce 'more crop per drop'. Demands for alternative products such as biofuels and traditional and 'health' foods (especially non-GMO) accelerated. External (especially inorganic) inputs were becoming increasingly expensive due to the reducing perceived and actual availability of petro-carbons; and Humankind was rediscovering its need to balance or replace hedonistic pursuits with better nutrition, mental stimulus and spiritual peace, while contemplating the possibilities inherent in Space exploration.

What is currently known as 'modern agriculture' is built on a physico-chemical understanding of soil that marginalises the soil's biological actors and factors. Although in recent years the centrality of biological actors in soil systems has been increasingly acknowledged, the scientists of tomorrow will need to go beyond the "post-modern" attempts to mimic forest systems and take into account the importance of values such as poverty reduction, environmental conservation (including above- and below-ground biodiversity) and equitable food distribution. Due to costs and availability, scientists will need to find ways of:

- preventing and rectifying, for example, soil compaction, salinity and acidification using natural processes;
- revisiting Liebig's Law of the Minimum, taking into account not just soil but other yield determinants such as the availability of finance, labour, fuel and other external inputs, cultural norms;
- enabling both small- and large-scale farmers utilise the second paradigm of Sanchez (1994): Rely more on biological processes by adapting germplasm to adverse soil conditions, enhancing soil biological activity, and optimising nutrient cycling to minimise external inputs and maximise the efficiency of their use.

To meet these complex challenges soil scientists of the 21st century will need to become more holistic in their approach. While continuing with physical, chemical and biological research they will need to utilise dynamic simulation and modelling to further their understanding of the interaction of these with one another as well as other components of the production cycle. While working in close association with for example anthropologists, sociologists, economists, entomologists, plant pathologists and weed and other crop agronomists they will need, as John Hanks once put it, to 'keep one foot in the field'.

In addition to 'pure' scientists, 'Specialist Generalists' need to be developed - holistically well-informed scientists who hear the needs of advisers and farmers then get out there and discover root causes with scientists and representative farmers and advisers, developing possible solutions, testing them in the laboratory or research station, suggesting alternatives which farmers can compare for themselves, then disseminating results effectively to all potential users, not least those training or in-training. Purposeful effective 'lobbying' of politicians and other opinion leaders combined with consumer marketing will be required to ensure that these efforts are funded, that their results remain in the public domain, and that short and long-term considerations influence decision making.

In the mid-1950s a school of thought existed which believed that the soil's primary function was to anchor plants. We know that soil is not just a haphazard jumble of particles but a complex dynamic biological system including many organisms not yet named, let alone understood, especially in relation to one another. Superficially we have seen how soil disturbance destroys soil structure, but only now are we starting to appreciate how important that structure is - not just for the entrance and penetration of air, water and roots, but also for the maintenance and robustness of especially the meso-micro-bio-system, and the effect that that in turn has on nutrient and water availability and consequently root and plant growth and crop yield. Despairingly we have tried to replace natural processes with quick-fix solutions - earthworms with subsoilers, predators with pesticides. As a result, topsoil has been blown or washed away, pests have proliferated, costs have escalated and, in many instances, yields declined, and the primary function of the soil scientists of the 21st century is going, through listening, logic, research and communication, to be to grow their own understanding and that of farmers, advisers, consumers and politicians of the soil complex and its critical importance to human survival on this planet.

Acknowledgements

Many friends and mentors from many continents, cultures and schools of thought have contributed to my understandings. Some will agree with what I have said, others may be diametrically opposed, but I would like to thank them all, especially those who took the time and trouble to respond to my request for 'Help!'. Their number is legion, their intellects profound, their search for Truth exemplary, but to acknowledge them by name would be unfair to those who perforce would be left out. So please, my colleagues, be content with a heartfelt Thank you!

Reference

Sanchez, P.A., 1994. Tropical soil fertility research: towards the second paradigm, Transactions 15th World Congress of Soil Science. ISSS, Acapulco, pp. 65-88

♦

The future of soil science: the role of soils for the society and the environment

Emmanuel Frossard

ETH Zurich, Institute of Plant Sciences, Experimental station Eschikon, P.O.Box 185, 8315 Lindau-Eschikon, Switzerland. E-mail emmanuel.frossard@ipw.agrl.ethz.ch

During the last century mankind has appropriated a large proportion of the environmental resources. This domination resulted in a strong increase in fluxes of nutrients and contaminants in the environment, in a decrease of natural resource reserves (e.g. groundwater, oil, phosphate), in pollution of water, air and soils, in soil degradation and even in some cases in the disappearance of rare soil types, in increased urbanization, in the reduction of biodiversity, and in an increased occurrence of natural catastrophes and of human health problems. These changes are summarized under the term "global change". The various aspects of global change will be further exacerbated as world population will increase from 6 to 9 billion. Food production must be doubled by 2050 to meet the needs of the growing population. Agricultural production has mainly to increase in developing countries. New striking aspects of agricultural production are the rapid increase in surfaces planted with genetically modified crops and the strong increase of livestock production. All of these changes will directly or indirectly affect soil properties and functions.

Whereas the consequences of global change on climate, air quality, on water quality/quantity and on biodiversity are being largely discussed in the public and receive attention from funding bodies, the importance of the soil is less recognized. In industrialized countries this lack of awareness is related to several factors. Food is abundant and it can be imported from other countries and therefore soil is not any more recognized as an indispensable basis for food production. In contrast, soils can be traded as substratum for buildings and streets, in some instances at very high prices. On the other side, although soil fertility is highly valued by smallholders from the tropical and subtropical areas for food production, the lack of finances hinders investment in any soil amelioration techniques that will only pay off in the future. Finally, the other functions of soil in addition to food production are hardly known to the broad public unless they get lost.

Soils are natural resources that are not renewable at the human life timescale. Their properties and management must be considered in any sustainable development schemes. The challenge is to use soils such that the needs of humankind can be met without compromising the needs of future generations.

What and how can soil science contribute?

It is still necessary to explain the different functions of soils within the soil science community, to other scientists, teachers, decision-makers and to the public. Political decisions must be taken before dramatic problems like the dust bowls in the 1930s in the USA! This requires on one side solid research activities in soil science and on the other side a continuous dialogue between soil scientists and the society. The recent development of the European Strategy for Soil Protection during which soil scientists and decision makers were involved in a dialog on soils with the public is in this respect a good example.

Rigorous and high quality research is, and will remain, the basis of soil science. Covering the different needs of society in a sustainable manner can only be based on a thorough knowledge of soil properties and functions. A lot of excellent research has been done in the different subdisciplines of soil science but there is still a lot to do to improve our understanding of processes controlling soil development and functioning. In particular, research is needed to understand the possible effects of global change on the soil properties and functions (e.g. on weathering, on water and element fluxes, on soil biodiversity etc.) so as to adapt land use and management to new situations. More research is also needed at the interface between soil science and other scientific disciplines including geology, geography, biology, agronomy, social sciences and economics. Finally, the results of these interdisciplinary studies will need to be further integrated, not only conceptually, but also in numerical models. This integration will allow to obtain a shared idea about the systems under study and to make predictions e.g. on the effect of political decisions or of the changes in economic conditions on soil properties and functions. These research activities, either oriented to a better understanding of soil functioning and/or better soil management, must be undertaken at all levels, from the laboratory and field to the global scale. They must be carried out worldwide including scientists from developing countries in efficient networks as the International Union of Soil Science. The soil science community must contribute more actively to international initiatives. The involvement of the International Union of Soil Science in the International Council of Science on the role of Science for Health and Well-Being and in the International Year of Planet Earth of the United Nations are good examples.

Information derived from research must be made available to the scientific community, to soil users (farmers, agronomists, foresters, civil engineers) and to the society. We must be able to convince politicians to adopt pro-soil measures. As politicians should take decisions based on the need of people, citizens need an appropriate education to soils not only at the university level but also in the secondary and in the primary schools. It is a continuous duty to convince citizens that the ground they walk on, they build on, on which they leave their wastes, is one of the basis of life on this earth. In Switzerland, although soil protection is anchored in a federal ordinance, almost one square meter still disappears each second under constructions. The total surface of abandoned industrial sites amounts to 17 millions m^2 which is equivalent to the total surface of the city of Geneva. This is a large potential to be used before construction expands onto new sites. A large proportion of the agricultural soils are affected by erosion and compaction and 10,000 ha have too high concentrations in contaminants. Not only the role of soils must become part of the societal dialog but science-based solutions must be implemented to ensure their sustainable use!

Acknowledgements
The author thanks Dr. A. Oberson (ETH Zurich) for the fruitful discussion on this paper.

◆

Future of soil science

C. Gachene
Faculty of Agriculture, University of Nairobi, P.O. Box 29053 – 00625, Nairobi, Kenya. E-mail: gachene@uonbi.ac.ke

Hoping that there will be future! The future is bleak. During the late 1970s and early 1980s, there was recognition of soil science and there were many soil science field activities for rural development, such as irrigation schemes. Funding was not a problem and students' enrolment at the postgraduate level was not a problem either, neither were scholarships to undertake postgraduate studies in soil science uncommon. Today, it is a different in Kenya. Soil science at the university where I am teaching is at the danger of extinction. Postgraduate students are very few. During the re-organisations of departments soil science departments were the first to be merged with others. This is despite the importance of soil science in agricultural production.

The following are some of the reasons given for lack of enthusiasm in soil science:

- Diminishing donor support in the field of soil science compared to other fields of agronomy. This has affected both research and capacity building (human and equipment);
- Lack of recognition at policy level on the importance of soil science;
- Lack of job opportunities;
- Lack of support of local and regional soil science societies that are expected to bring soil scientists together thus enhancing information exchange. Talk of clubs with diminishing memberships!
- Review of curriculum to get out of traditional soil science that seems to be not so friendly and popular with the students.

Suggestions on the way forward

Ways should be explored of supporting soil science, especially in the developing world. Although most of the agricultural projects are donor driven, we should not overlook the importance of soil science. In Kenya, the Rockefeller Foundation was a major supporter in soil science until 2004 when funding for the themes addressing soils came to an end. Can we strengthen joint research projects that address soil issues which may be easier to attract funding?

Until governments recognize the importance of soils and soil science, this field will continue to be endangered. A small team of concerned people is currently working on a policy paper on soil fertility issues in Kenya. We see some future here as this will lead to the recognition of soil science. Once done, job opportunities are likely to be forthcoming. No wonder most countries lack coordination units/bodies to know who is doing what in soil science related fields.

Soil science societies

Being a former Secretary General of the Soil Science Society of East Africa (SSSEA), one of the major challenges was to bring local scientists together and the lack of support to hold conference. Should the IUSS be assisting such societies in identifying potential donors? I feel so. Indeed it is such regional bodies such as SSSEA, which is giving the morale that all is not lost in soil science. IUSS Working Groups, should, as much as possible, incorporate members from developing countries. Lack of information flow can also be a hindrance to appreciating soil science. New developments in soil science should filter to as many soil scientists as possible.

I do foresee the future of soil science if the science is integrated with other fields. For instance, should we not start looking on soils in relation to environment? We should get out of the traditional soil science. Revision of old curriculum is thus necessary with a view of re looking the role of soil science and the society in general. I feel this will make soil science to be more attractive. The future is not so bright if it is business as usual of traditional soil science. In a country like Kenya, soil science has a major role to play in most environmental issues and more support for soil science is needed.

◆

Future of soil science

Sabine Grunwald

Soil and Water Science Department, University of Florida, P.O. Box 110290, Gainesville, FL 32611-0290. USA. E-mail SGrunwald@ifas.ufl.edu

To address the future of soil science requires understanding its historic roots, societal needs and knowledge gaps. This brief article provides an outlook on the future of soil science in a post-modern technology-driven world that is faced with limited earth resources.

Soils vary gradually in geographic space and through time and form complex patterns in dependence of multiple interrelated environmental factors and anthropogenic and natural forcing functions. Soil research has been focused on the genesis of soils, their composition, factors that influence them, and their geographical distribution. Numerous specialized soil science sub-disciplines have developed including soil mineralogy, microbiology, chemistry, physics and pedology, to name a few. This segregation into separate units has generated detailed understanding of soils. Future challenges will include unifying soil science knowledge within the discipline and other closely related disciplines, such as hydrology and environmental sciences, to move toward understanding the complex ways in which various separate earth compartments are interacting with each other at landscape scales. Soil scientists will need to effectively participate in interdisciplinary studies without loosing their own roots and identity. It will be important that soil scientist play an active role in generating datasets and information but also in transfer and share knowledge with stakeholders, decision makers, land use planners, politicians and others. Soil science must continue to expand beyond its traditional identification with agriculture as it becomes a partner in the earth, ecological and environmental sciences.

Multiple conceptual soil-landscape models have been developed to formalize knowledge on soils. For example, factorial soil-formation models use functions to relate environmental factors such as climate, topography, land cover, geology, and others to soils. Historically rooted in geology and anatomy, numerous soil taxonomies have been developed. Soil surveys have been focused on mapping of morphological soil characteristics and taxonomic classes derived from field observations. This double crisp approach segregates the soil continuum into crisp map units (polygons) and aggregates multiple soil characteristics to derive taxonomic data. Numerous soil classification schemes are used world-wide to group soils into different categories. But it might be too simple to assume that we can accommodate the needs for society by aggregating pedon descriptions and taxonomic map units often too coarse for site-specific applications. The demand for high-resolution, site-specific soil attribute data is enormous to address a variety of local, national and global issues. These include, but are not limited to, precision agriculture, assessment of environmental quality, conservation management, sustainable land resource management, carbon sequestration and global climate change and others.

Global connectivity, knowledge and information sharing have motivated holistic studies that focus on understanding functional relationships among ecosystem components. In this context, soil science plays a major role providing knowledge on soil patterns, processes and landscape dynamics. Ecosystem services characterize the functions that are useful to humans and contribute to ecosystem stability, resilience, sustainability and integrity. These services are diverse ranging from physical (e.g. best management practices that reduce nutrient leaching) to socio-economics (e.g. crop production, cultural values) and aesthetic aspects. Ecosystem services provided by multi-functional and multi-use landscapes are affected by the type, intensity, and spatial arrangement of land use and human activities as well as soil-landscape properties. Soil science has the potential to contribute to the valuation of ecosystem services.

There are four major areas that have contributed to a gradual shift from qualitative to more quantitative soil-landscape characterization:
1. Novel mapping tools and techniques such as soil sensors (e.g. electromagnetic induction, diffuse reflectance visible/near/mid-infrared spectroscopy), global positioning systems, airborne and satellite based remote sensing, and Light Detection and Ranging (LIDAR), etc.
2. Data management - Geographic Information Systems and database management systems,
3. Computing power to process multidimensional environmental dataset and
4. Methods - advanced multivariate statistical and geostatistical methods, three-dimensional reconstruction techniques to create soil-landscape models, and algorithms that describe pedogenic processes. Digital soil mapping and modelling techniques have shown much promise for rapid and cost-effective soil mapping at high spatial resolutions covering large regions. These methods often combine advanced mathematics and statistics to process comprehensive, multidimensional environmental datasets in concert with measured soil observations. A comprehensive overview of digital soil mapping and modelling was presented by McBratney et al. (2000; 2003) and Grunwald (2006).

Pedometrics, defined as the application of mathematical and statistical methods for the study of the distribution and genesis of soils, will play a critical role to shape the future of soil science. It integrates soil science with other disciplines such as GIScience and mathematics and facilitates spatially and temporally explicit mapping of soil attributes. In 2004, pedometrics was adopted as a new Commission of the International Union of Soil Science. A more quantitative approach to soil science will enable to close knowledge gaps and improve our understanding of pedogenic processes at micro-, meso- and macro-scales, non-linear behaviour of ecosystem processes, biogeochemical cycling at multiple spatial and temporal scales, and assess effects of human activities and natural forcing functions on soil quality. To incorporate uncertainty into soil science applications will be important to optimize sustainable land resource management. Although generic relationships between soil attributes and environmental factors have been identified, they are domain specific and may change through time. Thus, no universal equation or model exists that fits all soil-landscapes. There is ample opportunity for soil scientists to fill these research gaps using deductive and inductive scientific techniques.

Interdisciplinary educational programs will be pivotal to train the next generation of soil scientists. Future soil scientists require broad training rooted in traditional soil science (physics, chemistry, microbiology, and pedology) complemented by analytical, quantitative and geospatial modelling skills. The web-based distribution of 2D soil maps and data will continue to play a major role to disseminate information widely. Scientific visualization and reconstruction techniques to create 3D and 4D soil-landscape models will facilitate to better communicate knowledge on soils to the general public. Finally, we should not forget that the future of soil science does not only dependent on data and facts but requires genuine motivation and enthusiasm for the subject matter.

References

Grunwald, S. (ed.), 2006. Environmental soil-landscape modeling – geographic information technologies and pedometrics. p. 488. CRC Press, New York.

McBratney, A.B, I.O.A. Odeh, T.F.A. Bishop, M.S. Dunbar, and T.M. Shatar, 2000. An overview of pedometric techniques for use in soil survey. Geoderma 97: 293-327.

McBratney, A.B., M.L. Mendonça Santos, and B. Minasny, 2003. On digital soil mapping. Geoderma 117: 3-52.

♦

Future of soil science

Alfred Hartemink

ISRIC – World Soil Information, PO Box 353, 6700 AJ, Wageningen, The Netherlands. E-mail alfred.hartemink@wur.nl

It is not easy thinking about the future without considering the past and current trends. So I will give some wobbly ideas on the future as a little extrapolation of the present and past, and then about the future without thinking of those – the independent imaginable future of soil science. Finally, something about the IUSS.

Soil science has always had two ways of thinking: to show how the world is working, and show how the world should be working - and change it. It has been good in both but there has been a shift towards the second way of thinking, emphasising the usefulness of our activities. Related to this is that over the last half of the 20th century the soil science community has been diluted by an influx of persons attracted not by science as vocation, but as a source of money and jobs (Philip, 1991). A generation is retiring and there are few new positions created. Less soil science is now being conducted than 20 to 30 years ago and yet the number of publications increases each year. It may be that soil science is done more efficiently as computers are involved all the way from data collection up to electronic publishing. It may be that we are just recycling ideas.

Globally, there has been, and will continue to be, massive land use changes driven by population growth, climate change and increasing globalisation. Just like companies move their factories around the world in search for the highest economic return, so agriculture is moving to areas where it can produce the largest returns. In many temperate regions that means decreasing areas under agriculture; in tropical regions food production has to increase. Soil information is essential in both regions. We can't stress that enough but we rely on old data, some dated observational techniques and in particular, our mindset. There are new sensors and there other types of observations like genetic sequencing of samples (not species) that will speed up understanding of soils (Gewin, 2006) and can be more linked to some of the soil prime functions (e.g. medium for plant growth, filtering and buffering, C sequestration etc.). They are not routinely used yet but a revolution in observational techniques is on the doorstep.

I believe it was Keynes who said that the difficulty lies, not in the new ideas, but in escaping the old ones which ramify into every corner of our minds. Somehow we are looking at soils in the same way as we did 100 years ago. Just suppose that soil science had to be started today, that we knew nothing about soils nor had any idea how to research it. What would we do?

Would we treat soils as we would treat plants, animals and the whole earth system? Would we try to devise systems of classification searching for discrete units? Would we measure a set of individual properties, combine those, link it and derive some wisdom from it? It is hard to come up with answers that are freed from our thinking into textural triangles, horizon differentiation or C fractions. In any case, if soil science would be invented today it would be more independent from agriculture – at least in those parts of the world where food is ample. Perhaps we come up with a whole new set of differentiating properties and their measurements that do not fit ClORPT thinking.

I cannot imagine that we can do good soil science without field and laboratory experience. However, computer skills are becoming increasingly important and in science degrees the importance of maths and chemistry will be taken over by computer skills. But the thinking has to remain and that is the most difficult part to stimulate and as in any science: too little thinking obstructs progress.

To some extent soil science is a victim of its own success, globally there is enough to eat (but very unevenly distributed) and with an increasing urban population insulated from the soil, knowledge and interest in the soil is diminished. The coming generation (possibly female dominated) is not necessarily excited by the presence of cutans in the lower Bt horizon. They have other thrills driven by technological gadgets like the synchrotron, sensors for mapping earthworms or software that roams the web for data and builds new data infrastructures. They can also be driven by societal concerns. There is the danger that the new generation may fall in the same pit as the one they had escaped: If the information and wisdom obtained by new methods is not labelled and communicated as generated by soil science, it will not be recognised by other disciplines. That is a danger.

Something about the IUSS

There are three roles for the IUSS. First, cement the global soil science community together - this traditional role is increasingly important now many soil scientists are part of other departments or have been relabelled. Secondly, the IUSS should increase the recognition of soil science amongst the scientific community. That is partly catered for by the ICSU membership and the International Year of Planet Earth. Thirdly, the IUSS has to play a key role in informing the general public and politicians – many of which are estranged from the soil.

There are other things that the IUSS should do. The World Congress of Soil Science held every four years might not remain attractive in the long run. Many people prefer different type meetings for better interaction with other disciplines just as they also publish increasingly in journals other than primary soil science journals. The IUSS might co-organise the World

Congress of Soil Science with other unions to start and foster interaction; for example with IGU (International geographical Union), INQUA (International Union of Quaternary Research), ISPRS (International Society of Photogrammetry and Remote Sensing) and but also the chemists (IUPAC) and physicists (IUPAP). So instead of choosing a country for the next World Congress the IUSS should choose a scientific union. It formalises what is already happening on the ground and might contribute to an enhanced soil science identity.

Furthermore, the IUSS should become a professional organisation with a permanent secretariat, a non-amateur website and a smarter strategy to interact with the aboveground world. That costs money and will cost members too – doing less might cost more.

References

Gewin, V., 2006. Discovery in the dirt. Nature, 439: 384-386.

Philip, J.R., 1991. Soils, natural science, and models. Soil Science, 151: 91-98.

◆

Future of soil science

Christian Hartmann
Institut de Recherche pour le Développement, Ecole normale supérieure, 46 rue d'Ulm - 75230 Paris Cedex 05, France. E-mail christian.hartmann@ird.fr

The 'Millennium Ecosystem Assessment' (MEA) ordered by the United Nations was published in 2005 (www.millenniumassessment.org). More than 1,000 scientists from 90 countries worked 4 years to compile data about different ecosystems. They assessed the impact of human activities and possible scenarios of future evolutions. Soil is a fundamental compartment of most ecosystems, and it is possible to link some of our research activities with their impacts on environment and society and see what the soil science future could be.

The document reports the success of agriculture in feeding the growing population - success for which soil scientists can partly be credited. The success was achieved by bringing natural ecosystems into cultivation. More land was converted to cropland since 1945 than in the 18th and 19th century combined. Moreover there has been simultaneous intensification of production (Green Revolution). High food production being achieved with high inputs to the soil (water, fertilisers, energy, etc.). Those drastic changes have also some collateral effects: degrading soils through medication of natural biogeochemical cycles (acidification, salinisation, erosion, etc.) and decreasing resilience. In degraded soils, recycling of agricultural (or industrial) inputs was limited. Consequently many by-products were released in other environmental compartments which have thus also been degraded (sediments infilling reservoirs, chemicals transferred to under ground water, etc.). For the future, all scenarios predict that soil productivity will decrease in tropical areas, and that pollution by nutrients loading will increase (medium to high certainty) while population (and its food requirement) will continue to grow (more than 50% being in Asia).

In this context, soil science will have i) to increase soil productivity to maintain food production, ii) to rehabilitate degraded agroecosystems iii) to avoid 'collateral effects' and iv) to provide techniques of sustainable soil management economically acceptable. To increase soil productivity, previous soil scientists had larger flexibility as they had only an economical constraint which was that management needed to be profitable. Nowadays, we have an economical constraint plus an environmental one. Simultaneously our world is facing a shortage of water and oil - main inputs in modern agriculture. Because mining of natural resources is no more acceptable, food production can only be achieved through improved recycling (Fig. 1).

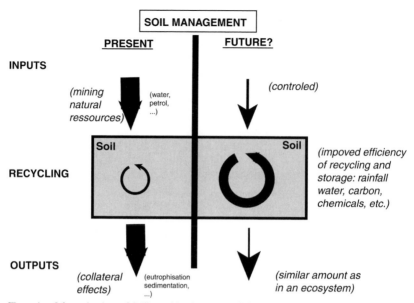

Figure 1 – Schematic view of Soil's position in present (left) and future (right) agriculture, the latter being required by society for environmental reasons. Soil science will be asked to understand and control the internal recycling and storage processes; fluxes will probably be economically estimated and integrated in financial analysis concerning agricultural managements.

Under tropical conditions, some natural ecosystems present high recycling capacity and high biomass production if compared to their production potential estimated from soil analysis. Soil scientists should probably dedicate more attention to such systems and study recycling processes to emulate them in cultivated environments. In natural environments, spatial heterogeneity and biodiversity seems to be major conditions of high productivity. For example, in West Africa discontinuous crust on soil surface induces runoff and water drainage in the more porous areas where mineral elements and carbon can accumulate and consequently plants can grow: despite seemingly insufficient average rainfall, spatial heterogeneity concentrated the resources and allowed localised cultivation. Rather than describing average soil characteristics and related properties, future soil scientists will have to describe spatial heterogeneity as well as relations and feedbacks between the different compartments of the soil system. Soil biological activity (vegetal and animal) being important factors for soil recycling process will probably be intensively studied.

Understanding and describing natural systems will allow soil scientists to suggest soil management techniques stimulating or emulating similar processes in context of agroecosystems. In the past, several attempts have been made to increase complexity of cultivated systems (alley cropping, associated plants, earthworm introduction, etc.) but efficiency seemed rarely high enough to compete with traditional monoculture. This is partly because simply introducing a new element without creating interrelation and feedback with other compartments has limited efficiency. If similar attempts were based on sound and larger knowledge of relations in natural ecosystems, they could probably be more successful. Finally, because of global warning, agroecosystems will also have to face new and erratic (warming will not be linear) conditions in a near future (drought/flooding, higher/lower extreme temperature, increased rainfall intensity, etc.). It is important that soil management can stimulate soil resilience potential under variable climatic constraints.

Soil scientists will have to focus on conditions and processes of soil resilience in natural environment to introduce these aspects for alternative management techniques. For several reasons, such alternative management would not be profitable in the on–going economical system in which agriculture and forestry are involved. But a big change has perhaps started in 1997 when an international agreement has been signed concerning a price of Carbon circulating in the environment (around 300 €/t CO_2). Some years ago the land value depended on its production potential, now it will depend also on his carbon storage and recycling potential. Because biodiversity is also considered as important, negotiations have already started to estimate its financial value! Calculating monetary value for environmental compartment or quality could be a revolution able to change global perception of soils and lands. Other environmental aspects will probably be 'economically estimated' like, for example, the capacity to resist erosion and avoid sediments release. Economist and 'environmentalists' will expect soil scientists to provide quantitative information on aspects rarely measured yet. Schematic agro-ecosystems as presented on Fig. 1 will not only be characterised by fluxes and interrelations, but also by several financial evaluations. Because this affect farmers' practices, soil scientist have to be involved in the economical evaluation in order to favour management that has positive impacts on the environment and food production.

In conclusion, I believe that future soil science will probably be a more complex an integrative science than presently, having a wider scope with a multidisciplinary approach able to associate traditional aspects (physics, chemistry, etc.) with more innovative ones (soil ecology, 'soil economy', etc.). We, soil scientists, have to be in a leading position to respond the challenges of the 21st century. Our success might not depend on technical improvement but rather on a shift in some of our basic concepts and paradigms.

♦

Future of soil science

Juan José Ibáñez

Centro de Investigaciones sobre Desertificación (CIDE), 46470 Albal, Valencia, España. E-mail juan.ibanez@uv.es

It is difficult to be a fortune teller in such a rapidly changing world. After a period of bonanza under the umbrella of the agronomic paradigm, soil sciences and, in particular, pedology began to suffer a crisis that still persists. To overcome this situation, we need to broaden the boundaries of our discipline to meet the social demands of soil information and, at the same time, regain the trust of scientific policy managers, colleagues in other disciplines and the public at large. Environmental deterioration and the preservation of natural resources are pressing issues that call for re-formulating the aims of pedology. But, in this endeavour, it is not enough to mobilize new information technologies, because maximum efficiency cannot be obtained from new technologies without a conceptual change optimizing the advantages they provide. Otherwise, as Peter Burrough reminds us that maximum efficiency cannot be obtained from new technologies without a conceptual change optimising the advantages that they provide. Almost fifteen years later, such a conceptual change is still a pending task.

In the "anthropocene" we are so drastically changing the land surface that we are obliged to study, describe and classify materials, processes and structures that beforehand did not occur in nature. We need a revised concept of soil that will broaden the old conceptual barriers and open new horizons. In and around cities, the soil cover is modified by sprawling construction projects and waste disposal facilities that create new soil genera (urbisols, technosols). We also have practically no knowledge of the processes occurring in lake sediments and other water-submerged areas, including the photic zone of the continental shelves (hygric soils). Likewise, from scientific and social demand standpoints, the lower soil boundary should be extended to cover the regolith. The concept of soil-regolith system is validated by the fact that biological activity exceeds the boundaries of what textbooks usually describe as soil, several metres deep. The soil-regolith system, the wetland areas and the urban soils are the places on earth that are most exposed to pollution resulting from the increasing quantity of waste of all sorts and their uncontrolled disposal. Several authors have suggested reconsider and broaden the definition of the soil concept on the basis of these new challenges (see Ibáñez & Boixadera 2002, among others). Science is progressing as much or more because of the heuristic potentiality of daring hypotheses than for technological changes themselves, however important they may be. This enlarged soil concept requires classifications based on new criteria. The WRB has proven to be a step forward by taking into account wetlands, urbisols and technosols, although it suffers from a "non vacuous" definition of soil and does not consider the soil-regolith system.

Currently, universal soil taxonomies are very much questioned by some pedometricians and by the defenders of the so-called "soil quality paradigm". The former propose that we leave everything in the hands of mathematicians, while the latter are selling old wine in new bottles. The former attack the artificial nature and subjectivity of traditional classifications; the latter address certain environmental and agronomic issues using new methodologies, instrumentation and an anthropomorphic vocabulary (functions, health, quality, soul, etc.). This questioning of the classical conceptions lacks epistemic rigor and good knowledge of the scientific method. Both fall into the technological paradox referred to by P. Burrough. Universal soil classifications are completely necessary, inasmuch as they are a language amongst specialists of one and the same discipline, as well as comprehensive storage and retrieval systems. They could be supplemented, rather than replaced, by an international nomenclature code (INC) as is done in biological taxonomies. National soil classifications should be subjected to such if we do not want to keep on living in a Tower of Babel, while ad hoc classifications may be required to cope with specific applied research problems. In any event, I believe that to draw up new classifications without studying what is happening in other disciplines is a big mistake. The human mind has potentialities and limits for memorizing and processing information. We must learn what is known of the human mind in order to process information inasmuch as a classification, or taxonomy, is retrieval information systems in a fast and user friendly way, accepting partitions in hard classes and hierarchical taxonomies, irrespectively of the continuum dilemma.

The technological-conceptual paradox arises when implementing soil information systems Do we have enough soil data, and appropriate soil data, to contribute to the variety of application fields emanating from an increasing societal demand? It might be of concern that so much time, effort and money are devoted to obtaining soil information indirectly (e.g. via pedotransfer functions, taxotransfer rules, predictive digital soil mapping, etc.), instead of harvesting adequate novel field soil data. Information technologies cannot operate indefinitely only on the basis of remotely-sensed or inferred data. Updating soil inventories is one of the main fields where new technologies should facilitate data samplings and acquisition. Work needs to be carried out with non aggressive techniques with a view to obtaining the most detailed information as possible, as well as three dimensional information on the soil-regolith system. Soil monitoring programs need to start from updated soil inventories, more detailed than the existing ones in many countries. In other words, we urgently need more and better field data to improve the IT efficiency for predictions and simulations. Exposure to collecting field data is also important in soil training programs to avoid blind computerized data manipulation.

I detect a growing obsession with problem solving (applied science) to the detriment of theoretical studies. Basic and applied research should go hand in hand, since the latter must be supported by the former if we wish to improve our doctrinal corpus, instead of accumulating data without formalizing them into new disciplinary knowledge. Soil is part of our natural heritage and therefore needs to be preserved both in its diversity and in its most pristine natural state possible. The immense soil biodiversity is practically unknown. A fascinating new adventure is to get ourselves into the main stream of conservation biology, which includes both living organisms and their habitat (soil types), and contribute to the design and implementation of soil reserve networks. The relationship between human health and soil will prove to be another promising field of exploration and someday we may be able to speak of pedomedicine. Developments in molecular knowledge and instrumentation level can help improve our understanding of biological processes of the soil system.

New information technologies are changing the panorama of teaching and publication of results of research and we pedologists need to take advantage of all their potential. "Open Access" movements are fast growing in the international scientific community. New developments in soil science should be within everyone's reach, particularly in less favoured countries where limited access to scientific advances threatens to widen the gap between rich and poor countries. On-line courses and implementing scientific documentation depositories on Web pages and portals must continue to grow in an exponential fashion. The dissemination of science from children's to higher education levels also has to be much improved. The best way in which citizens of all ages see the value of what soil science provides to society and learn of the capital importance of soil in the biogeospherical system is through rigorous and amenable dissemination of relevant information. Economic ways are weblogs, see for example http://weblogs.madrimasd.org/universo/ It is having success in Latin America. It helps create citizen awareness and call the attention of decision makers responsible for formulating and implementing science policies.

Acknowledgements
I would like to express my appreciation to Dick Arnold, Alfred Zinck and Juan Sánchez for their inestimable collaboration in reviewing this manuscript's content and form.

♦

Future of soil science: a Canadian perspective

Yash P. Kalra

Canadian Forest Service, Edmonton, Alberta, T6H3S5, Canada. E-mail ykalra@nrcan.gc.ca

The study of modern soil science is believed to have its origin in the mid-17th century. For most of the succeeding three centuries, the main goal of soil science was to increase yields of agricultural crops. The latter half of the 20th century was also impacted by non-agricultural concerns, such as those relating to forests and environment. The application of soil science principles in the enhancement of forest fibre production, and in remediation of soil contaminated by solid, liquid, and gaseous pollutants are on-going thrusts at the dawn of the 21st century. In this century, soil scientists will face many challenges besides those that have been inherited from previous decades. Nine years ago, I prepared an article for the Indian Society of Soil Science (Kalra 1997). The following items include ideas from it together with additional reflections since.

1. One of our major challenges right now relates to the cause and effect of climate change. Soils represent the largest C pool in the world and we need to understand and manage soil C to provide a significant stabilizing buffer and to provide a land-use planning framework for responding to climate change. All of this must be accomplished within a setting of ever-increasing climatic instability and human pressure for food stability. As organic matter is at the centre of most soil functions, more efforts will have to be devoted to the understanding of its nature, dynamics, role, and management.
2. The most fundamental challenge locally and globally is: How to convince society that knowledge of soil science and soil management is seriously under-utilized to the disadvantage of national and local economies?
3. Today soil scientists are concerned about the future of soil science at universities. The challenge for scientists is to assert soil science as an independent discipline with a coherent body of knowledge about natural bodies on the landscape. Soil science is perceived as an adjunct of plant science. It is being fragmented and dispersed among disciplines such as engineering, biology, chemistry, agriculture, and forestry. Such fragmentation must be resisted by firm knowledge of the discipline.
4. Support for applied and basic research is one of the most highly leveraged investments that any government can make. Research funds, however, virtually in all science disciplines are now scarce and becoming scarcer.

5. Significant increase in population worldwide is projected for the 21st century and, therefore, food production (especially in developing countries) will remain a concern. Increased attention will have to be given to the supply of micronutrients in our soils as we continue to step up yields by use of large applications of the major nutrients. Research efforts need to be intensified in precision agriculture and nutrient management.

6. It will be necessary for soil scientists to increase their understanding of the forest soil system. Whereas the purpose of forest soil research in North America may be primarily fibre production, population pressure, mostly in developing countries, will increase the amount of forest land converted to agriculture. The effects of clear-cutting of forested areas on soil and water conservation, as well as on communities, require more attention. One area of forestry that is going to have serious ramifications for forest soils is the use of forest biomass for bioenergy. There are some implications regarding nutrient depletion and soil disturbance, particularly in the boreal forest.

7. Environmental concerns will not only continue but will increase as society demands more growth to achieve and maintain a higher standard of living. Further growth leads to higher consumption and waste disposal. Containment of toxic substances will continue to present challenges to soil scientists. Pollution of soil and water from pesticides, herbicides, nutrients, heavy metals, and municipal, farm, and industrial wastes are examples. Bioremediation will be one of the important research directions.

8. Soil scientists in the 21st century will have to become more process-oriented in the application of their knowledge. Besides finding the solution to a problem, the questions of "how" and "why" will become as important as the solution.

9. High class, productive land is being used for industrial and residential development and, since this commodity is finite, it should be protected. The continuing problem of an exploding population and ever-diminishing arable land resource must receive prompt attention to avoid increasing risks of mass starvation in many parts of the world.

10. Water management will play a significant role. The word *blue* (blue revolution) will join *green* (green revolution) as an environmental buzzword.

11. Our goal must be to disseminate information to researchers, extension personnel, users of land resources, especially soils, and the general public. Strong international collaborations among soil scientists will have to be developed to address common problems.

12. The long-term experiments, such as those carried out at the Breton Classical Plots (http://bretonplots.rr.ualberta.ca/) in Alberta, continue to impact our communities environmentally and economically. These experiments assess the interactions of crop productivity, soil quality, and the environment. We must continue to support these efforts.

13. There is a need to develop a strong mechanism to promote soil science education to teachers and students in schools.

14. Most soil scientists are now in the public sector. There is a growing tendency for the public sector to shrink. I see soil science moving further into the private sector.

15. Soil tests will be more of a monitoring tool and less of a diagnostic procedure. There is a need for validated methods and increased participation in the proficiency testing programs.

The future of soil science is promising. It is our responsibility to manage, use, and protect the soil resources for future generations. We look forward to meeting the challenges in the 21st century.

Reference

Kalra, Y.P. 1997. Challenges facing soil scientists in the 21st century. Indian Society of Soil Science Newsletter, 3: 1-2. New Delhi, India.

♦

Pedology in interdisciplinary studies for environment and material sciences

Selim Kapur
Departments of Soil Science and Archaeometry University of Çukurova, Balcali 01330, Adana, Turkey. E-mail kapur@cu.edu.tr

The subject to highlighted for the future of soil science, I believe, is related to the sequestration of carbon in soils and it's implications to climate change. Soil information, today, is sought and believed to fill in the breach in the global/local climate change studies, which approach and methodology-wise are wandering in a sphere of uncertainties (the unknown) and enigmatic attempts in predicting future climate changes with minor considerations regarding the past. The capacity of the soil to sequester C and its resilience in the soil should be considered as the prime factor of constructing sustainable land management programmes. Moreover, the preparation of country or region-wide soil C-distribution maps leads to a basis for developing sustainable land management programmes.

As we look forward to how people will manage the earth's soil resources in the future, it is important to reflect on how it was done in the past so that lessons of history are learned and not forgotten. For example, the study of P fractions, clay mineral types, weathering levels of feldspars to kaolinite and thermoluminescence properties of quartz and feldspars throughout the soil profiles of man-made terraces, and their fluctuation indicate past climate changes but also past cultivation techniques. The study of the soils developed at man-made wall terraces and man-made mounds are also rewarding in the sense of obtaining data on soil formation relevant to climate changes that may bear clues for the future.

Another area of concern is Aeolian materials. The individual grains of the wind-blown Saharan dust materials have been studied by pedologists and sedimentologists for their mineral contents varying at different transportation episodes from northern Africa to the Mediterranean basin. However, soil scientists seeking to conduct further studies on wind-blown materials dedicate themselves to understand the scavenging properties of the aerosols, which is a rising concern in the prevention of air pollution and the continuity of the humidity cycle throughout the mid-latitudes of both hemispheres

The archaeometry perspective

The visual front of soil science-micromorphology with the capacity to overlook the physical side and fabric and microstructure of the materials in nature, which are related to soils and sediments, such as rocks, and especially ceramics and construction materials, at macro and micro scales is probably one of the most rewarding fields of economic significance. The conception and aptitude attained by many soil micromorphologists on the visual assessment of the colours and shapes of the objects in soils, and the natural or artificially induced progress of their formation processes has provided the means to interpret the precarious and doubtful features despite the aid provided by sub-microscopy. These features include the minerals neo-formed at high or specific temperatures, especially developing in ancient and contemporary ceramics, pottery and similar functional materials.

The determination of the stress coatings in several ancient ceramic shards similar to the stress coatings developed in soils by the shrink-swell phenomena is a striking example. Stress coatings have been determined to develop in clay-rich raw material sources (soils/sediments) used for the production of ceramics during the firing process of increasing – decreasing temperatures, especially at the ancient buried 10th and 11th Century Seljuk kilns. Coatings of illuviated clay were also determined in Hittite and Neolithic Çatalhöyük pottery, which may indicate the minor climatic fluctuations of the Early to Late Holocene.

Applications of micromorphology

How soil is structured and its architecture and fabric at the micro level have been the central focus of micromorphologists. Given the role of organic matter and other constituents in aggregate formation and the implications for structural stability for cropping sustainability, the role of microstructure in relation to cropping impacts on soils needs elucidation. Of particular interest is low organic carbon, sequestered through legume-based rotations affecting micro-structure.

◆

Research for sustainable soil management

Dominique King
Institut National de la Recherche Agronomique, Science du Sol - InfoSol, Centre de Recherche d'Orléans, BP20619, 45166 Olivet, France. Email king@orleans.inra.fr

Since 1970, several world summits have highlighted the limits of the planet resources and the impact of human activities on the evolution of these resources. Gradually the international community increased awareness for the biosphere (deforestation, biodiversity decline), atmosphere (air pollution, climate change) and hydrosphere (quantity and quality of water). At the interface of these major compartments of the environment, pedosphere remained ignored in spite of the central role it plays between these spheres.

It is now well recognised that soil, all over the world, is affected by human activities. Recently, the European Union launched a large public consultation with all concerned stakeholders to define a political strategy for soil protection. Soil functions were listed: biomass production, geochemical recycling, carbon sequestration, water regulation, etc. and were analysed in relation with the other terrestrial compartments and taking account of human needs. The different threats for soils (e.g. erosion, compaction, loss of organic carbon, contamination, salinization, sealing) were also analysed in order to improve understanding and, in return, to propose environmental actions.

Soils and their management

From this analysis, three questions can be highlighted:
(1) Are present soil maps and databases sufficient to describe the diversity of soils and of their functions?
(2) Are we able to deliver periodic and quantitative information on soil evolution and soil processes at global scale?
(3) How can we optimize human activities according to the spatial variability of soils with the aim of a contribution to the sustainable development?

(1) Diversity of soils and of their functions
In the 20th century, national and international survey programs were conducted to assess soil spatial variability. Large discrepancy between countries remains and there is a lack of data harmonisation. Moreover data are often old, seldom updated and most of the surveys are presently stopped. Research issues about soil mapping concern both the past and present of soils. We have to understand the origin of the variability of soils, and to use this knowledge to predict the current soil functioning. Variation

was already an issue during the first pedogenesis studies. It needs to be revisited through new numerical techniques, especially with 3D pedogenetic models combining probabilistic and mechanistic approaches. Prediction of current soil functioning relates to soil inventory programs. They are based on systematic analysis, according to a scale fixed in advance. They may be too rigid to answer future requests. We have to propose multi-sites and multi-scales approaches with new metrological tools adapted to the areas considered and to the required precision. The objective is to provide farmers or decision makers with numerical maps showing the soil functions in time and offering interactivity to examine scenarios.

(2) Soil evolution under the impact of environmental changes
Soil is a living medium in equilibrium with the other compartments of environment and in perpetual renewal at various scales of time. Possible impact of climatic change and human activities change increases the question of the protection of soil resources from short to long term scale. Research issues concerns observation of changes in soil components and soil properties under the impact of new environmental constraints (short term) and modelisation of soil evolution through pedogenetic processes in order to be able to assess long term soil modifications. We have to emphasize biological component of soils through the interaction between the physical and chemical components. It is essential to evaluate how soils are resistant against changes, or resilient, or evolving out of control, to identify possible feed back between soil components.

If knowledge about the soil resources is poor on a global scale, knowledge on soil evolution is even more reduced. Moreover, information is scarce with very few national systems of soil monitoring and even less at the global scale. They consist in a few multi-local monitoring programs which are rarely multi-purposes. A spatial generalisation of results is uneasy because of the diversity of pedological situations. Then, quantifying soil evolution needs a spatial approach led in concomitance with the multi-scale mapping works mentioned above. Moreover soils are archives from the past and a spatial analysis may lead to better understand soil evolution. These points reinforce the need to develop new soil mapping methods from a dynamic point of view. In all cases, the implementation of a global soil monitoring system, as it has been done for other environmental resources (atmosphere, sea environment), would permit to explore the diversity of situations and thus to better understand the processes in question, and to provide a quantitative picture of soils evolution at a worldwide scale.

(3) Spatial and sustainable management of soil resources
In the past, soil was mainly considered as the support of agricultural production. This objective implied programs of soil improvements (e.g.

drainage, tillage) and supply (e.g. nutrients, water). These actions succeeded in achieving their objectives but sometimes with detrimental effects on other soil functions that affect environment and soil degradation. Research issue are (i) a global evaluation of soil functions (including biomass production), (ii) and a spatial land management answering both at the social and environmental issues. The spatial scale can vary from the field for precision agriculture to a region for agro-environmental rules. We therefore need spatial and temporal databases provided by new survey and monitoring programs presented above. This will also require a fine knowledge of the instantaneous state of soils (especially water conditions) to gradually optimize practices over time. Such an approach requires an increasing coupling between more and more powerful metrological networks and soil functions models in interaction with the other compartments of environment. Researches have to be led to develop the use of new information and communication technologies (remote sensing, geophysics, GPS, network).

Soil is a continuum in space and time. An integrated approach at the various scales will be necessary to consider sustainable soil resources management. This will require the development of measurement networks to better take into account the soil diversity and to optimize human activities according to the pedological constraints and to the safeguard of their multi-functionality. In return, the pooling of these networks will offer to science new means to explore a large range of situations and to better understand the spatial functioning of soils in relation with the other environmental compartments. Finally, these networks could be shared by a large range of users and perhaps participate to the social development of rural areas.

Acknowledgement
I thank my colleagues Dominique Arrouays and Guy Richard for their contribution and encouragement to this paper.

◆

Views on the future of soil science

Guy Kirk
Cranfield University, Cranfield MK43 0AL, UK. E-mail g.kirk@Cranfield.ac.uk

One of the most difficult aspects of soil science is the wide range of scales it encompasses, both spatial and temporal. It covers spatial scales from the molecular to the landscape, often together in the same problem, and temporal scales from instantaneous processes to soil formation processes lasting millennia. Continuing explosions in the availability of information at both ends of these scales will greatly influence the future of soil science. At the small end are the various molecular biological sciences – genomics, proteomics, metabolomics – and at the other end there are the geospatial sciences – remote sensing, geographical information systems, Earth Systems Science. Soil science overlaps with and links many of these disciplines. There will be increasing demand and opportunities for soil science to exploit this information and a future thrust must be to provide quantitative frameworks to link together the various threads.

Traditionally this would have been done with statistical procedures to establish empirical relations between variables, as done very successfully for agriculture in the past, for example in deriving fertilizer recommendations based on field trials covering the various combinations of crops, soils and climates. But for environmental problems and emerging new biological and other technologies, this approach has both practical and scientific limitations. The main practical limitation is that with models based on statistical correlation, predictions can only be made by interpolation within established data sets. Each new problem therefore requires a new set of trials or experiments and establishment of a new set of empirical relations. In view of the great diversity of environmental problems and technologies and the rapid pace of change, this is impractical. The scientific limitations are that statistical relations are not cause and effect relations though they may indicate what causal factors need to be considered, and they are poor at revealing the sorts of non-linear relations and feedback processes that are common in natural systems.

So it will be important to develop predictive soil models for problems at different scales based on mechanistic understanding of underlying processes, and as far as possible independent of statistical correlation. In the past models for 'decision support' have often been overly simplistic or conjectural and insufficiently well corroborated against experiments. 'Process oriented' decision support models have been developed which purport to account for the processes thought to be important in particular systems. But to the extent that the input parameters of such models are derived from the output, the whole process is little better than an elaborate form of curve fitting. Models are needed that are as mechanistic as possible and corroborated against experiments in which the input parameters are measured independent of the output. New mathematical and computing tools are available for this, and new experimental techniques are available for testing models.

Dealing with scaling issues will be central to progress in modelling. Properly corroborated models of particular processes can be used as sub-models in larger-scale models, coupled to datasets at the available resolution. But this process of 'up-scaling' or 'down-scaling' brings with it particular problems associated with error propagation and interactions between variance in input parameters and non-linearity in models. For example, there may be discrepancies between the spatial scale at which a process is modelled (e.g. the pedon), the scale at which information on input variables is available (e.g. a generalized value for a soil map unit) and the scale at which a policy maker needs to make decisions (which may be field scale, farm scale, regional/ catchment scale or national scale). Such discrepancies cause particular problems when the model depends non-linearly on key variables or additional processes intervene at scales between the pedon and the unit of interest. The application of geostatistical methods and the techniques of spatial analysis to such issues will help resolve some of these difficulties.

In parallel with this there will be an increasing need for high-resolution soil information with national and international coverage to drive models and to monitor soils on a national basis. Advances in computing power and geostatistical techniques offer enormous potential for this, for example in digital soil mapping in which fine resolution soil information is interpolated from coarse resolution information using terrain, geological and other data. All this must be underpinned by a better understanding of the biophysical processes that drive soils: physical, chemical and biological.

Funding for soil research is surely on the brink of resurgence. Soil issues continue to move up the political agenda as the environment becomes increasingly prominent in national and international politics, and protection of the soil for its own sake increasingly has the same status as protection of the air or water. Further, Earth Systems Science has emerged as a mainstream topic, and the fundamental role of soils in it is widely acknowledged.

In summary, the future of soil science looks very good.

◆

Future of soil science: soil science research at universities in the USA

Mary Beth Kirkham
Department of Agronomy, Kansas State University, Manhattan, KS 66506-5501 USA. E-mail mbk@ksu.edu

The future of soil science at universities in the USA will depend on funding. I have observed soil-science research since I was a child, because my father, Don Kirkham, was a professor of soil physics at Iowa State University from 1946 until his death in 1998. After World War II until about 1980, funding of soil science at the Land Grant universities came from the federal government through formula funding. These funds were sufficient to cover graduate students. Foreign students, funded by their governments, used to come to the USA. They often were from oil-rich countries like Iran and Saudi Arabia. The Fulbright Program, which funds foreign students, and National Defence Education Act Fellowships, given to domestic students, were other sources of funding for graduate students.

These three sources of funds (formula funding; foreign government support; fellowships) have essentially dried up. Only a small amount of formula funding is available and is not enough to support a graduate student. Foreign countries no longer send their students abroad, because they, like the USA, are facing budget crises. The foreign students who do have funding, such as those in Iran, cannot get visas. Fulbrights no longer pay research expenses, so a professor has to have funding to support a Fulbright student.

Consequently, most graduate students must be supported by external funds that a professor obtains. Graduate students are necessary for the survival of departments. At Kansas State University, a department has to have at least 20 M.S. students and 5 Ph.D. students to maintain a graduate program (Dr. K.W. Williams, Kansas State University, March 21, 2006, personal communication). If this minimum is not maintained, the department will be eliminated. That is why heads, when they evaluate a professor, put the main emphasis on external grants. No job description today goes out without the line "must be able to get grants for an externally supported program." This was not a stipulation for employment 25 years ago.

In the 1980s and 1990s, when I obtained grants from the NSF and DOE, funding was based on peer review. Now much funding, if not most, comes from special appropriations. According to Feller (2004), by using earmarks, "Congress and the universities are increasingly working together to undermine fairness and quality in academic research and development."

The lack of governmental funding for science reflects the fact that taxpayers' money is now going for defence and security. It is predicted that the U.S. research workforce will decline (Showstack, 2004). What money is available for research goes for the new science (e.g., molecular biology; nanotechnology), which is perceived as being more valuable than traditional science such as soil science. Traditional areas of soil science may disappear. The University of Nebraska used to have a strong soil-physics program, but it no longer has a soil physicist.

So where will the support for soil science come from? Industry will continue to fund what it feels is necessary. Government regulations force industries to clean up polluted sites and soil scientists will be needed for cleanups. The soil scientists that survive are going to be those with political expertness, who get earmarks. This means people who do not have this proficiency, or do not wish to participate in political activities, will be cut out of science. Creativity is going to suffer, because soil scientists will need to spend their time with politicians rather than doing research.

The research that will be done will be applied and focused on immediate results, because industry, which will be the main funding source, requires this. Theoretical research will not be done, unless a soil scientist does this on his or her own with personal funds. Quantitative research will be focused around computers. Instrumentation is developing faster than the science to use it. For those who can afford the most recent equipment, they will be seeing the soil with greater acuity and measuring components with greater resolution.

While computers will be used to model, they also will be the cause of lost time. The time that soil scientists used to have to read the literature and do research is no longer available because they are striving to keep up with technology. Everyone spends hours a day answering E-mails, keeping computers free of viruses, installing and learning new software to stay up-to-date, and struggling to mount manuscripts on difficult Web sites run by publishers. We are accomplishing less than in previous years due to technology. My department has five people working to keep its computers functioning. These jobs did not exist 10 years ago. In the past four years, my department has lost three soil scientists, who have not been replaced.

Emphasis is now given on team projects. The individual scientist getting a federal grant is becoming a thing of the past. Some large projects do require team work. However, the individual scientist is still the one who comes up with new ideas. It is the individual scientist who gets recognition from a professional society. For example, membership in the National Academy of Science is given to only one person. Teams never become members together of the NAS.

Diversity is an issue that has not been addressed in soil science departments. One could probably count on the fingers of one hand the number of female, full professors of soil science at Land Grant universities. The federal government, due to its requirement for equal opportunity, is still the main place where female soil scientists work. Black scientists are also absent from soil-science programs. Scientists from Asia are now filling soil science positions, and this trend will continue. Diversity will be represented by them. In sum, I see the future of soil science at universities in the USA as follows:

1. Less funding
2. Funding available will be through special appropriations, which means soil scientists will to have to have political adeptness; those who lack political skills will have to find other jobs.
3. Loss of traditional soil science programs
4. Hiring and retention of women and Blacks will remain a challenge.

References

Feller, I., 2004. Research subverted by academic greed. The Chronicle of Higher Education, January 16, 2004, p. B6 - B7 + cover.

Showstack, R., 2004. National Science Board report indicates U.S. research workforce may decline in size. EOS 85(20): 198 (18 May 2004 issue) (one page only).

◆

Soil science in the era of hydrogen economy and 10 billion people

Rattan Lal

Carbon Management and Sequestration Center, The Ohio State University, Columbus, OH 43210 USA. E-mail Lal.1@osu.edu

Soil is the foundation of human civilization. Good quality soils have supported thriving civilizations which made notable contributions to science and culture. Societies which did not promote stewardship of their soils and natural resources vanished. Political instability, ethnic conflicts and horrific wars have been fought by civilizations faced with food scarcity and hunger caused by soil's inability to support their population growth. Indeed, "there are not many troubles in the world more alarming than those caused by fire in the pit of an empty stomach." The concept was appropriately summed up by O. Henry who stated "Love and business and family and religion and art and patriotism are nothing but shadows of words when a man's starving". Future threats to the world peace may also arise from the relationship of "human to soil" rather than "human to human".

The green revolution of the 20th century

Advances in production agriculture was one of the success stories of the 20th century. In the USA increase in grain yield from 1900 to 2000, respectively, was 1,500 to 8,400 kg/ha for corn (multiple of 5.6), 900 to 2,900 kg/ha for wheat (multiple of 3.2), 1,080 to 2,422 kg/ha for soybean (multiple of 2.2), 1,680 to 6,625 kg/ha for rice (multiple of 3.9) and 790 to 3,000 kg/ha for peanuts (multiple of 3.8). There were even more drastic increases in agronomic production in South Asia and China, which saved billions of people from hunger and starvation. While doomsayers expressed apprehension and pointed fingers, soil scientists, along with plant breeders and agronomists, ushered in the green revolution by enhancing agronomic production by growing input responsive varieties on fertile and irrigated soils. As has been the case in the 20th century, those holding neo-Malthusian views will again be proven wrong through adoption of recommended management practices for sustainable management of soil resources.

Emerging issues of the 21st century

Alas, impressive gains in food production in the 20th century were achieved at the cost of environmental quality. With agricultural expansion came soil degradation; with increase in use of agricultural chemicals came environmental pollution; with increase in irrigation came salinization; with deforestation and excessive ploughing came emission of CO_2 into the atmosphere; and with increase in production came excessive reliance on fossil fuel energy. Thus, focusing on improving the science of soil management for further enhancing agronomic productivity, soil scientists must also address other issues which are important to environmental sustainability, including: atmospheric enrichment of greenhouse gases and the attendant global warming, scarcity of renewable fresh water along with eutrophication and contamination of surface and ground waters, disposal of urban and industrial wastes, soil and human health, soil as repository of germplasm, along with the traditional functions of soil as foundation for engineering and civil structures, and source of industrial raw materials. There is a strong need to study processes governing interaction of the pedosphere with biosphere for enhancing agronomic and biomass productivity and improving biodiversity, with atmosphere to improve air quality and mitigate the greenhouse effect, with lithosphere for waste disposal and sequestration of CO_2 in geological strata, and with hydrosphere to improve the quality and quantity of renewable fresh water resources. Therefore, future researchable priorities are (a) maximizing agronomic and biomass productivity per unit input of water and chemicals and energy, (b) minimizing environmental pollution, especially water pollution and soil contamination, (c) moderating climate through soil and terrestrial C sequestration, and (d) using soil as a medium for waste disposal. Studies of linked cycles of carbon (e.g., biosynthesis, respiration, mineralization and humification), water (precipitation, evapotranspiration, infiltration, runoff) and nitrogen (biological and industrial fixation, leaching, volatilization) are of a high priority.

Building bridges across disciplines
Soil scientists must reach out to other disciplines to effectively address environmental issues, and to broaden the scope of their research beyond the use of soil as a medium for plant growth. Soil scientists need to work with colleagues in basic sciences (e.g., hydrology, climatology, geology, ecology, biology, chemistry, physics) to understand the mechanisms underpinning soil's ecosystem services. They must work with colleagues in applied sciences (e.g., economics, political science, social sciences) to address the human dimensions of the decision making process. By so doing, soil scientists will be positioned to serve the emerging needs of human society during the 21st century.

Education
Soil science curricula at undergraduate and graduate levels must be relevant to prepare soil scientists for addressing the emerging global issues. Conventional curricula in the land grant colleges are often weak in basic sciences (e.g., physics, chemistry, mathematics, biology, hydrology,

climatology). The conspicuous lack of these courses in curricula does not prepare students from agriculture and natural resources for undertaking basic research related to climate change, hydrological and ecological processes, chemical transformations, water quality, elemental cycling and other processes governing ecosystem services and resilience. There is also a strong need to train soil scientists in communication skills to effectively interact with scientists in other disciplines, policy makers, funding organizations, industry stakeholders, and public at large. The curricula must prepare scientists in adopting a holistic approach to the study of soil, not only for agronomic productivity and food security but also for addressing relevant environmental, engineering, biological, ecological, archaeological, planetary/astronomical, social and political issues. They must be able to address inter-disciplinary problems by looking beyond the discipline of soil science and working with colleagues in other sciences.

Soil science issues

A major shift in the paradigm for soil scientists, especially those in the developing countries, is to undertake demand driven projects with innovative and original approach. The importance of scientific contributions depends on the originality, dedication and problem solving skills of soil scientists. Scientific rigor and quality are always enhanced by bigger and tougher challenges, which are going to be in abundance in the world of 10 billion people, and scarcity of natural resources which are already under great stress. Five among numerous challenges of global significance to be addressed are:

(i) Global Food Security. The global average cereal grain yield of 2.64 Mg/ha in 2000 must be increased to at least 3.60 Mg/ha by 2025 and 4.30 Mg/ha by 2050. With possible changes in dietary habits in emerging economies such as China and India, the average cereal grain yield will have to be increased to 4.40 Mg/ha by 2025 and 60 Mg/ha by 2050.

(ii) Biofuels. In addition to advancing food security, soil scientists must play a major role in producing feed stocks for biofuels (bioethanol, biodiesel) and H_2 cells which is the most versatile energy storage and carrier system. Soil scientists need to work with engineers to enhance conversion efficiency from sunlight to H_2. The conversion efficiency may be better for biomass generated as agricultural by-products (bagasse, food packing/processing).

(iii) Waste Disposal. Soil scientists will need to take an active part in developing waste disposal technology. The so-called "waste" can be converted to value added products as soil amendments. Composting and landfills can be used to generate biogas, soil fauna can be used to degrade pollutants, and termite colonies in soil can degrade wood fibre and cellulosic materials.

(iv) Water Purification. More than per capita arable land, scarcity of renewable fresh water will be a major challenge in numerous countries in the arid and semi-arid regions. Judicious management of soilscapes within a watershed will be necessary to improve and enhance water resources. Developing improved practices of watershed management are also needed to reduce the problem of hypoxia in coastal ecosystems.

(v) Soil and Climate. Historically, world soils have been an important source of the enrichment of atmospheric concentration of CO_2 and other greenhouse gases. In addition to soils and biota, fossil fuel combustion became a major source of CO_2 with the onset of industrial revolution. However, land use management systems must be developed to make world soils a major sink for atmospheric CO_2. Further, changes in soil quality because of projected change in climate must be assessed and considered in developing systems for sustainable management.

Soil and the future of human civilization

Feeding world population of 6.5 billion in 2006, 7 billion in 2010, 8 billion by 2025 and 10 billion by 2050 and beyond mandates that soil quality be restored and enhanced. Food insecure population of 850 million in 2006 and increasing, along with several billions suffering from hidden hunger, leave no cause for complacency. The projected food grain deficit of 23 million Mg by 2010 must be met through improved systems of soil management, and adoption of land saving technologies through agricultural intensification in sub-Saharan Africa and elsewhere where extractive farming is widely practiced.

World's energy demand at 400 Quads/yr (1 Quad = 10^{15} BTU) is increasing. Alternatives to fossil fuel must take effect in the coming decades. Biofuels, and H_2 produced from biomass, are important sources of energy supply during the 21st century and beyond. Carbon sequestration in terrestrial ecosystems is another option of off-setting fossil fuels. Developing technologies for establishing biofuel plantations on degraded and marginal soils is a win-win strategy.

For issues of meeting the food demand, improving the environment, enhancing water availability and quality, and achieving energy security, the answer is the soil. Soil scientists have an opportunity to rise to the occasion and meet these challenges.

♦

Clarifying misperceptions and sharpening contributions

Henry Lin

Dept. of Crop and Soil Sciences, 116 A.S.I. Building, The Pennsylvania State Univ., University Park, PA 16802. E-mail hul3@psu.edu

A major road block in advancing soil science is the negative perception of soil held by the general public and the scientific community at large. The public view of the soil is generally associated with "dirt," "mud," and "farming," leading to low esteem, low appreciation, and thus low priority. In reality, however, the soil is the foundation of diverse ecosystems, the basis for the flourishing of life on earth (when combined with water), and a global security issue. As Daniel Hillel (1991) succinctly pointed out, "Our own civilization is now being tested in regard to its management of water as well as soil." The earth's fragile skin regulates the land surface's mass and energy balance, but has long been taken for granted, especially following the Industrial Revolution. The soil-related issues abound even in urban environments, including waste disposal, pollution prevention, stormwater management, green space, building foundations, and land use.

In the scientific community, the soil is commonly viewed as "simple," "easy," and "invisible," leading to over-simplified approaches towards studying vastly heterogeneous and dynamic geoderma, and the neglect of the hidden but hard-to-renew treasure underfoot. Science published a special issue in 2004 (Vol. 304, Issue 5677) on "Soils – The Final Frontier" suggesting that, after 500 years since Leonardo Da Vinci, the ground beneath our feet is still as alien as a distant planet. It is intriguing to ponder why. Is extraterrestrial exploration more urgent than our home planet's exploration and protection? Why so many critical phenomena in soils are still "mysterious" (e.g., underground microbial biodiversity and subsurface preferential flow patterns)?

I suggest the following three steps to help propel soil science forward – provided that we act forcefully and sharpen our contributions to the society and the science at large:

Address misperceptions

Much can be done and needs to be done in this regard. For instance, innovative visualizations can be used to reveal the complex world underfoot. An excellent opportunity is the Smithsonian Soils Exhibit scheduled to open in 2008, where interactive movies, multimedia presentations, and live demonstrations can be used to educate and impress millions of people around the world about the challenges and rewards of exploring the soil.

Another appealing approach is the use of the earth's Critical Zone concept to help raise the awareness and regard of soil and to publicize career opportunities in working with soil. The Critical Zone, being that part of the earth from the top of trees to the bottom of aquifers (NRC, 2001), contains the entire pedosphere as its central foundation. Interactions at these interfaces between the solid earth and its fluid envelopes determine the availability of nearly every life-sustaining resource, and provide the foundation for all human activities. Hence, the Critical Zone concept provides a comprehensive framework for integrated studies of water with soil, rock, air, and biotic resources, and justifies the need for sustainable funding and continued supply of future soil scientists. To advance soil science, I also believe in the merit of distinguishing pedology from the general term of soil science, because a crushed sample of soil is as akin to a natural soil profile as a pile of bricks is to a beautiful building. The traditional way of studying soils using glass beads, beach sands, ground-sieved soil materials, or isolated soil columns should be replaced more with *in situ* soils that have distinct characteristics of pedogenic features, structures, layers, heterogeneity, dynamics, and landscape context.

Form alliances with other disciplines
Coupling, scaling, and forcing are three recognized fundamental scientific issues across many disciplines (NSF-CUAHSI, 2005). Hence an integrated, multidisciplinary, and multiscale approach is needed to advance our ability to forecast and plan for global changes and to address critical societal issues such as human safety, human health, economic development, and sustainability. Traditional discipline-limited and individual component-based approaches to measuring, modelling, and predicting pedological, hydrological, and biogeochemical processes need to be replaced by integrated studies of soil, water, and biogeochemistry. In fact, the interactions of soil and water are so intimate and complex that they should not be studied in a piecemeal manner, but rather as a system across spatial and temporal scales. Biogeochemical cycles are inseparable from the hydrologic cycle and the critical reservoir of the soil, thus indicating the fundamental importance of integrated studies for the fluxes of water, energy, and chemical elements. As water has been recommended as a unifying theme for research and education on complex environmental systems (NSF AC-ERE, 2005) and the Critical Zone provides an attractive framework for integrated studies of natural resources and the environment (NRC, 2001), allying soil science with hydrology, biogeo-chemistry, and other related bio- and geosciences will prove to be fruitful.

Enhance soil science contributions

Within the framework of integrated Critical Zone exploration, soils play 7+1 roles – from basic geoscience, to hydrological, ecological, atmospheric, agricultural, engineering, environmental sciences, and to extraterrestrial explorations (Lin, 2005). Such an inclusive vision for integrative soil science helps enhance its image in the scientific community at large. In the meantime, we need to sharpen the tools used to map, monitor, and model integrated processes in the pedosphere, and to enhance the contributions of soil science to the society. An excellent example is Selman Waksman, a soil microbiologist, who won a Nobel Prize in Physiology and Medicine in 1952 for his discovery of the antibiotic streptomycin, which was the first drug to show value in treating tuberculosis. We now know that amidst the vast number and variety of microorganisms in soils are a host of microbes now valued for their potential to help solve environmental problems and supply cure as well as disease (such as botulism and anthrax). Another example is the soil-forming theory of V.V. Dokuchaev and H. Jenny, which has had profound impacts in the field of geography, geomorphology, ecology, Quaternary geology, and paleopedology. A third example lies in land-use decisions and "smart growth" planning, because new land-use plans and land development practices should consider the manner in which natural soils vary over the landscape, which offers clues as to "what" can best be done and "where" with the lowest risks and the greatest opportunities (Bouma, 2006).

In closing, I hope a clear image of *food on our table, water in our bottle, and air in our room* can be well connected to the nature's gift to us that we call soil, and that a compelling case can be made to promote the integrated studies of the earth's *Critical Zone* in order to advance soil science and sharpen its contributions to the society and the science at large.

References

Bouma, J., 2006. Hydropedology as a powerful tool for environmental policy research. Geoderma 131:275-286.

Hillel, D., 1991. Out of the Earth – Civilization and the Life of the Soil. The Free Press, New York.

Lin, H.S., 2005. Letter to the Editor on "From the Earth's Critical Zone to Mars Exploration: Can Soil Science Enter Its Golden Age?" Soil Science Society of America Journal 69:1351-1353.

National Research Council (NRC), 2001. Basic Research Opportunities in Earth Science. National Academy Press, Washington, D.C.

National Science Foundation Advisory Committee for Environmental Research and Education (NSF AC-ERE), 2005. Complex Environmental Systems: Pathways to the Future, Washington, D.C.

National Science Foundation – the Consortium of Universities for the Advancement of Hydrologic Science, Inc. (NSF-CUAHSI), 2005. Cooperative Large-Scale Environmental Observatories (CLEOs). Interim Science and Implementation Plan. Washington, D.C.

♦

Perspectives and future orientation of soil science

Franz Makeschin

Dresden University of Technology, Pienner Str. 19, D - 01737 Tharandt, Germany. E-mail makesch@forst.tu-dresden.de

Soil science inheres an unique intermediate function in research and environmental education. It connects multiple facets of ecological sciences with those which deal with water, atmospheric and bio resources. Soil science contributes consistently to sustaining of life resources like food, habitation, recreation, industrial activities and transportation. Soils are an important key of landscape elements and therefore an important prerequisite for the internalization of costs and benefits in socio-economic land-use analysis.

During the last century soil science strongly developed their assignments. In the first phase discipline-oriented approaches with the classical sections like soil physics, soil chemistry, soil biology, soil geology or soil classification prevailed. Following process-oriented aspects played an increasing role considering the growing demands for understanding the functions of soils for crop production and the environment. These activities are impressively reflected in numerous peer-reviewed scientific articles, textbooks, and applied contributions. However, despite the indubitable achievements of soil science upcoming demands in respect to sustainable manage our natural resources, to mitigate environmental problems and hazards and to fight worldwide soil degradation are major challenges remaining.

In conjunction with these demands, soil science has to further contribute to an overall understanding and problem solving. Therefore it is essential to advance our knowledge both in basic and applied aspects and especially in transfer concepts for management, environmental assessment, administration and education. Special consideration should be given to an attractive student education and advanced training not only by loco, but also by distant education which even allows reasonable access of target groups in margin regions.

Some outstanding themes are sustainable land use approaches, integrative indicators of soil degradation, and both ecologically efficient and economically viable approaches methods for soil protection. For tropical and subtropical regions innovative and significant classification systems for fertility and re-gradation assessment, for up-scaling and regionalization, and for significant soil information systems by combining terrestrial experiences and modern remote techniques.

Beside the ecological and management-related view superior importance for a sustainable land-use should be given to necessary planning tools, to socio-economics and to acceptance-aspects for different target groups. Overall, concepts should connect research and environmental education.

National soil science societies should identify and implement research priorities within the framework of the IUSS under special consideration of inter- and intra-disciplinary research areas. As key research areas the following themes are emphasized:

- Soils, land consumption, land rehabilitation and recycling
- Soils and climate
- Soils and land-use
- Innovative and integrative methods in soil research
- Soil research in national and international infrastructure
- Soils in education, advanced training and society

♦

Musings on the future of soil science (in ~ 1 k words)

Alex. McBratney
Faculty of Agriculture, Food & Natural Resources, McMillan Building A05, The University of Sydney, NSW 2006, Australia. E-mail Alex.McBratney@usyd.edu.au

My instinct tells me, don't do this! Why not? I have a faint recollection of skimming through an essay by the British Nobel laureate, scientific philosopher and author of clear prose, Peter Medawar, who said that predicting the future of any science is doomed to failure. As I recall he gave a philosophical argument supporting this position. It roughly goes like this. From his point of view, science is about the acquisition or discovery of new knowledge about nature – not simply about logical corollaries of existing knowledge. This knowledge comes from formulating and testing *new* hypotheses or ideas - if I tell you now what these new concepts will be, then logically they cannot be new in the future. So given this argument, based on a fairly strict definition of what science is attempting, the future course of science can't be predicted. So Medawar's position was unequivocal, if anyone asks you to prognosticate about science, the simple and sagacious advice is - don't do it.

So, out of some sense of abandon I find myself doing exactly that which is apparently philosophically irrational. Ah well, here goes.

To begin, a quotation:

> *...as we know, there are known knowns;*
> *there are things we know we know.*
> *We also know there are known unknowns;*
> *that is to say we know there are some things we do not know.*
> *But there are also unknown unknowns –*
> *the ones we don't know we don't know.*

This was (in)famously said by Donald Rumsfeld the US Defence Minister at a Whitehouse press briefing on February 12th 2002. What has this got to do with the future of soil science? Well, a fair bit. Many have pooh-poohed this outburst as ill-advised, inarticulate, or just incomprehensible. I feel however, it gives us some clear categories of knowledge which we can use to think about the future of any knowledge-based enterprise, be it psychology, sinology or soil science. We can organise and slightly extend Rumsfeld's categories by constructing a two-way table, thus.

Characteristics of extended Rumsfeldian categories of states of knowledge and their relation to (soil) science

	KNOWN(S)	**UNKNOWN(S)**
Known	*Category 4* ○ (Widespread) soil science knowledge or apparent knowledge. ○ How widespread is it? ○ How universally true is it?	*Category 2* ○ 'Normal research' ○ Filling in the gaps ○ Technologically aided ○ Predictable
Unknown	*Category 3* ○ Education –stakeholders? ○ Ourselves ○ The future generation ○ Policy makers ○ Needs coalescence and synthesis	*Category 1* ○ Medawar's view of the scientific challenge ○ The frontier ○ Unpredictable ○ The exciting future lies here

So like some beauty pageant of old, I'll reveal these categories in reverse order.

Category 4 (the known knowns)
This is the canon of soil science that all professional soil scientists more-or-less know. Now, and in the future we have to mull over all of this and check it for inconsistencies and erroneous concepts. Two possible examples. Isn't it time Jenny was superseded? (Some advocate an energy approach.) Is the concept of soil quality bogus or just a cul-de-sac? I think we should expend about 5% of our effort in this category. (At the moment it's probably <1%).

Category 3 (the unknown knowns)
This is clearly about education – making others aware of what we know and what we can do. First we need to coalesce and synthesise our knowledge – make it less piecemeal, and then disseminate it to our fellow scientists, the new generations, policy makers and the public. This is a big task given that in many countries the newer generations and our governments have become disenchanted with science. We need to expend 40% of our effort here!

Category 2 (the known unknowns)
This is what most people think of as research. It's about colouring in a black-and-white picture, or putting flesh on the bones, of our knowledge. Among the many known unknowns we know we need a through understanding of biological soil function, discovery of the real structure and function of organic materials, a quantitative theory (not description) of soil variation, and a way of successfully spatially and temporally aggregating and disaggregating soil properties and processes. Technology, facilitating new measuring machines and instruments, is a great aid here but it should not

drive the agenda. It can be a drug and we can become addicted and delusional. Technology is there to help us answer the questions, not to be an end in itself. About 50 percent of our effort needs to be placed here, but it shouldn't be much more than that.

Category 1 (the unknown unkowns)
This is Medawar's real science and real research. Hardly anyone works here out on the edge anymore – governments and institutions don't understand this place – it's difficult to get money to do this, but the perhaps it doesn't need money. We need time however and lots of it, because it requires deep thought. This is where the breakthroughs occur. The new ideas here will give the researchers of Category 2 something to do for 30 or more years after these advances have been made. Logically, I can't tell you what these will be, but they could be weird heretical things like bacteria produce clay minerals or soil thickness is a key control of the terrestrial ecosystem. We need to spend much more time thinking – and we need to devote at least 5 percent of our effort here.

I have concentrated on the science of soil science rather than the politics, sociology or economics. Clearly what actually happens will be driven by geopolitics with countries developing and unravelling rapidly, along with perceived human and environmental threats and challenges. Although we might think the canon of soil science is global, much of what has been achieved has arisen from local concepts for local problems, a particular kind of fertilisation, salinisation and acidification which may have different causes and solutions in different places. Although this will continue we will have to unite our knowledge and expertise to solve global problems of food, water and energy security and dynamic sustainability. We need a big soil science that is all-embracing and expansive to serve society. This will ensure our survival as a valued discipline. We can't afford to be inward-looking and contemplative. The number of soil scientists needs to rise faster than the world population.

I advocate a thoughtful, expansive, outward-looking view. Rephrasing the words of my compatriot Burns, *and forward 'though I cannot see, I guess and hope!*

Alfred asked for a thousand words, perhaps I should have painted a picture.

♦

A pedologist's view on
the future of soil science

Neil McKenzie

Bruce E. Butler Laboratory, CSIRO Land and Water, GPO Box 1666, Canberra, ACT, 2601. Australia. E-mail Neil.McKenzie@csiro.au

My perspective on soil science is from the integrative discipline of pedology and unavoidably Australian. The predominantly harsh landscapes of this continent have shaped life for hundreds of generations. Human impacts after colonisation some 60,000 years ago are disputed but systematic changes in fire changed vegetation and wildlife. More dramatic has been the short period of European settlement. While many European settlers had a good eye for the agricultural potential of land, most failed to understand limitations inherent to the often old and impoverished soils. In 1949, it led a prominent politician to conclude that "we could not have made a bigger mess of the soil of the country if its destruction had been carried out under supervision."

Soil science flourished in response to the obvious challenge. An energetic scientific community emerged, supported generously by governments and appreciative primary industries. They generated valuable knowledge that eventually combined with progressive social attitudes to result in better quality land management across large parts of Australia. However, many problems remain including unsustainable rates of soil erosion, widespread acidification, insufficient organic matter, contamination and salinity. While the scientific understanding of these problems is good, implementing solutions is difficult. A combined effort is required from individuals, communities, scientists, governments, and industries. The need to understand soil processes has been overtaken by the need to apply what we know.

However, the funding environment has tightened – it is strongly applied, short term, and commercial. Soil science is supported on the condition that it results in better management of natural resources and water resources in particular. The number of soil scientists engaged in research has declined and disciplines such as pedology have been severely depleted. This comes at a time when pedologists are needed to provide recommendations on *where* to locate particular systems of land management. There is also demand for predictions of soil function across landscapes at a range of scales to support simulation modelling.

Soil evolution and land management

An integrated view of soil processes is central to sound land management. Soil properties and processes fit into ecosystems and soil formation is a consequence of cycles and flows of energy, water, sediment, nutrients and other materials. The foundation of our integrated view must be an understanding of soil and landscape evolution over decades, centuries and millennia. This is not just a theoretical nicety for pedologists. It provides essential context and a benchmark for understanding how current land uses interact with the landscape (e.g. baseline rates of erosion, leakage of nutrients, equilibrium carbon concentrations). Too little soil science is framed within this context.

While we owe a great deal to Hans Jenny, the functional factorial approach no longer provides a sufficient theoretical framework for explaining soil formation, particularly in ancient landscapes where the timescales for soil and landscape development are comparable to those for biological evolution. Conceptualisations of soil and landscape development need to emphasize processes, system linkages and co-evolution rather than factors alone. Such a theoretical framework is more compatible with material budgets used in geomorphology, biogeochemical cycling, hydrology, hydrogeology and atmospheric physics. We have good starting points for developing an improved general theory of soil evolution but the definitive account is yet to be written. Benefits could include more effective interdisciplinary communication and better spatial prediction.

Measurement

Many practical problems require an ability to estimate fluxes of water, nutrients, solutes and sediments. An understanding of the drivers of change is also required. In most cases, a secure understanding can only be derived from measurements at long-term research sites. There is also a need to estimate the pre-instrumental record to set context. In many countries, the lack of long term ecological research sites (see www.lternet.edu) weakens our capacity to be definitive on a wide range of pressing environmental problems.

Generalizing from a few well studied landscapes to large regions remains a central challenge. In most countries, particularly those outside Europe and North America, existing soil surveys do not provide an adequate framework. New and practical methods of digital soil mapping have emerged during the last 20 years and they are starting to provide an alternative to traditional survey (www.digitalsoilmapping.org). However, progress is slow compared to the spectacular advances in monitoring of the land surface and atmosphere. Related technologies for spatial information such as Google Earth are simply remarkable and they have created expectations for soil information that are far beyond our capacity to deliver.

Our biggest hurdle is the lack of efficient methods for measuring the functional properties of soil at scales relevant to natural resource management. The revolution in environmental sensing and measurement is producing sensors that are smaller, faster, more energy efficient, wireless, and cleverly programmed. The Mars Rover is a fine example and excellent progress is being made in precision agriculture. However, measurement systems are needed for the full sequence of soil layers across a range of scales and not simply the soil core or profile. A priority is characterizing variation in hydraulic properties at length scales between 10–1000 m.

A few imperatives

Cooperation and effective communication with other disciplines is now essential. This requires mastery of one's own discipline. This takes time to acquire and it is easy to overlook aspects of soil science that either matured prior to the advent of electronic journals, or relied on oral scholastic traditions (e.g. field studies) that have been since disrupted. For example, our knowledge of pedogenesis in parts of Australia has gone backwards despite our best attempts to record what is known. The situation is complicated further because career paths are now less certain and few students assume that it will be their life long vocation. It is imperative for all of us to work hard to consolidate our existing knowledge and make it accessible to our students and colleagues.

I have barely made reference to large parts of soil science. I am sure exciting advances in soil science will come from molecular biology but speculations on that topic I leave to others. Finally, there can be no doubt about the fundamental importance of soil science. Human population growth and aspirations for western-level standards of living will ensure that food production, water supply, waste management and environmental quality will be the pre-eminent issues confronting nations in coming decades. Richter and Markewitz (2001) put our task in the clearest of terms: 'Managed well, soil circulates chemical elements, water and energy for great human benefit. Managed poorly, it is impossible to imagine an optimistic future.' We must ensure soils are managed well.

Acknowledgements
David Smiles and Richard Stirzaker offered helpful comments on an earlier draft.

Reference
Richter, D.D. and Markewitz, D., 2001. Understanding soil change. Cambridge University Press, Cambridge.

♦

The future of soil science

Ahmet Mermut

University of Saskatchewan, Department of Soil Science, Saskatoon. S7N 5A8, Canada. E-mail mermut@skyway.usask.ca

Soil science has made significant contributions to the quality of human life and has enhanced our understanding of soil resource management to meet our food and fibre needs. The ability to feed the population currently over 6 billion people has raised concerns on food security and soil science is one of the basic sciences that provide enviable progress in food security. This changing demand of society has spurred new areas of investigation such as global carbon cycle, soil quality in relation to water quality, land degradation, cycling of bio-geochemicals, etc.

There is an ongoing debate on the role of soil science in the society and societal responsibility to support science and such discussions are leading to paradigm shifts in institutions responsible for research and development. Although modern soil science saw its birth after the Second World War, it has faced with new challenges at the beginning of the new millennium that question even its relevance and need to sustainability of life on earth. Part of this dilemma has resulted from the fact that soil science did not establish its role in environmental studies, until recently. It is now well established that all environmental studies need fundamental understanding of the soil system, from atomic to global levels. The soil science community has made major inroads in this area of research.

A new set of clients now value soil information, the demand for more and better information has increased and information delivered in a more timely manner is being demanded. Since the 1980s, a dramatic change has taken place in our thinking about utilisation of soil and land resources. There has been an increased awareness of ecosystem health and maintaining the quality of the environment, and rate of resource consumption, even in developing countries. The concept of sustainable development initiated by the Brundtland Commission (World Commission on Environment and Development, 1987), together with Agenda 21 of the United Nations Conference for Environment and Development (United Nations Conference on Environment and Development, 1992), have played significant role in our activities in research and development.

Land degradation, especially those induced by humans, has become a serious concern affecting the livelihood of almost every person on the earth. From an agricultural standpoint of view land use is the major cause of declining soil quality. Studies, particularly during the last two decades, are pointing to a variety of negative impacts to global ecosystems, resulting in the decline in land quality, global warming, and even disappearance of species of plants and animals. Land and environmental degradation are the domains of soil scientists. This is an excellent example to integrate not only sub-disciplines of soil science but also other disciplines including sociological, ethno cultural, political, and economic considerations.

The need for soil information is becoming more important in terms of sustainable land management, ecosystem health, and cycling of biogeochemicals. Soil resource assessment and monitoring soil resources is entering a new era, in terms of quality of information produced by new information technologies through the use of Geographic Information Systems (GIS) and remote sensing. The need for soil information to support agriculture resulted in the teaching of soils as an integral part of the agricultural curriculum.

Despite the fact that many concepts, methodologies, and information have been taken from other earth sciences, such as sedimentary petrology, hydrology, geomorphology, and mineralogy, specifically to serve agricultural production. A major factor that is forging a better alliance is the impetus provided by global climate change studies that requires a better understanding, quantification of earth's surface processes, and global climate change. Soil carbon sequestration is becoming a strategy to achieve food security through improvement in soil quality (Lal, 2004). Although the need to ensure productivity of the soil has not diminished, the additional investigations to support global bio-geochemical processes will have far reaching benefits to the science as a whole.

New technologies such as stable isotope geochemistry (Landi et al., 2004), nuclear magnetic resonance (NMR), high-resolution transmission electron microscopy (HRTEM), atomic force microscopy (AFM), pyrolysis mass spectrometry and others have provided tremendous opportunities to study and widen our understanding of organic matter. Weiss et al. (1993) have provided a good example how information on soil stratigraphy can help to reconstruct the paleoenvironment of human civilization and land use system. Many recent works demonstrate how paleosols can be interpreted in the context of environmental change (Arnold et al., 1990). This supports the view that we need to give more attention to interdisciplinary research to accomplish our task as soil scientists.

As Yaalon (2000) expressed, many ancient religions recognized the importance of soils, and their customs evolved into a spiritual attachment of Life-giving Earth. But unfortunately the ancient and classical scholars did not work with the nature of soils.

References

Arnold, R. W., Szabolcs, I, and Targulian, V. O., 1990. Global soil change. Report on IIASA-ISSS-UNEP. Task force on the role of soil in global change. International Institute for Applied Systems Analyses, Laxenburg.

Lal, R., 2004. Soil carbon sequestration impacts on global climate change and food security. Science 304: 1623-1627.

Landi, A., Mermut, A. R., and Anderson, D. W., 2004. Carbon distribution in a hummocky landscape from Saskatchewan, Canada. Soil Sci. Soc. Am. J. 68: 174-184.

United Nations Conference on Environment and Development (UNCED), 1992. United Nations Conference on Environment and Development (UNCED). Rio de Janeiro.

Weiss, H., Courty, M. A. Wetterstrom, W., Guichard, F., Senior, L., Meadow, R., and Curnow, A., 1993. The genesis and collapse of the third millennium North Mesopotamian civilization. Science 261: 995-1004.

World Commission on Environment and Development, 1987. Our common future. Oxford Univ. Press, Oxford.

Yaalon, D., 2000. Down to earth. Why soil and soil science matters. Nature 407: 301.

◆

Future of soil science: fostering multidisciplinary linkages

P.S. Minhas
Central Soil Salinity Research Institute, Karnal-132 001, Haryana, India. E-mail psminhas@cssri.ernet.in

Soils, though undergoing continuous transformations over time, provides habitat to biotic life and a base for the development of civilizations. Studies of soils are now becoming increasingly important, especially in underdeveloped and developing countries like India where uncontrolled demographic pressures are leading to conflicting interests and competition from urban agglomerations and industries. A great deal of concern is being raised by researchers, planners, environmentalists and farmers alike on declining factor productivity in agriculture and loss of biodiversity due to soil related disorders, pollution of soils from geogenic and anthropogenic sources, erosion, water-logging, salinity and other related problems like decline in water and air quality. Restoration of the productivity of such degraded soils is not only an ecological necessity but a socio-economic imperative to ensure the livelihood security of the inhabitants. Soil scientists play major role to address these complex nature of environmental, biodiversity and land use challenges being faced by mankind now and in the future.

Amongst the soil degradative processes, water erosion, globally affecting more than half the area, has been recognized as the greatest threat to landscapes and ecosystems. Landscape watershed management now needs to move beyond problem definition and quantification to include for development, testing and validation of remediation strategies. Water is paramount for food production and all economic activity. With increasing demands from domestic and environmental sectors, it is becoming an increasingly scarce commodity for irrigation. Thus the goal of ensuring enough food production in the face of the forecasted scarcities would require the soil scientists to work with engineers in improving water use efficiencies and ensuring "more crop per drop" at system/basin level, and also improve the productivity of water-limited environments obtaining in dryland (rainfed) cropping systems.

Urbanization coupled with industrialization is also inducing huge production of anthropogenic wastes of complex compositions, leading to disposal problems. Changed lifestyles are triggering greater use of detergents, aerosols, and generation of wastes containing heavy metals, polymers, pharmaceutical ingredients etc. Soils are the ultimate sink for all these pollutants but their capacity to cope with them is finite. On the one hand there is increasing diversion of good agricultural lands for civilian purposes and on the other hand, shrinkage of land available as sink for these wastes. It is a therefore a double-edged threat. The scarcity of water and competing use for good quality waters is leading to increased use of marginal quality waters in agriculture along with the attendant problems of human and animal health, soil health, and loss in quantity and quality of crop produce. Addressing all these issues, calls for a more holistic, integrated and multi-disciplinary partnership of soil scientists with public health engineers, hydro-biologists and medical professionals.

Even though fertilizer and other inputs have often led to short term yields enhancements in many parts of the world, concerns are increasingly being raised about the eventual loss in soil productivity and biodiversity due to mining of nutrients caused by intensive cropping and little recycling of organics. To overcome multiple nutrient deficiencies and enhance soil organic matter content of tropical soils, soil scientists are working on newer approaches like integrated nutrient management, precision farming, conservation agriculture, organic farming etc. There are many other encompassing issues like global warming, multifactor modelling of complex soil processes, remote sensing and IT applications for land use planning, developing technologies for genetically modified crop-based systems that also require the broadening of current paradigm of soil scientists.

Nevertheless, to be more relevant to society, soil scientists must improve the extent and the content of the interface with the stakeholders i.e. farmers and also the planners and even politicians for making the results more accessible and attractive to the users. Additionally, they should expand their horizons to industry, medicine, urban planning, environment and ecology, animal health, biodiversity, waste management etc. All of these are, of course areas, which would involve many other disciplines including soil science.

It is imperative that soil scientists should transcend from the reductionist and isolated approach of concentrating mostly on agriculture and forestry as in the past and present. They must come forward to forge links to coordinate interdisciplinary opportunities in the above multi-enterprise areas. Evidently, a myriad of opportunities exist for the soil scientists to help improve management of soil and water resources. But let us reckon that soil is non-renewable source and thus strive to save this fundamental resource for the welfare of our future generations.

◆

Future of soil science

Rolf Nieder
Institute of Geoecology, Braunschweig Technical University, Langer Kamp 19c, 38106 Braunschweig, Germany. E-mail r.nieder@tu-bs.de

Soil is a life-sustaining, biologically active, porous and structured medium at the Earth's surface formed by mineral particles, organic matter, water, air and living organisms. Consisting of several horizons, soil regulates the supply of water and nutrients for the flora and microfauna and is therefore one of the basic compartments for ecosystems. Soil is of fundamental importance for the cycling of carbon, nitrogen and sulphur and determines the partitioning of water percolating to groundwater reservoirs or flowing to rivers and lakes. Soil acts as a living filter for numerous (in)organic wastes, immobilizes or detoxifies toxins, and renders pathogens harmless. Soil is a habitat and gene pool, serves as a platform for human activities, landscape and heritage and acts as a provider of raw materials. To enhance the soil's capacity to perform these functions, it is important to understand the factors and processes affecting soil quality under expanding and competing land use.

Soil science developed from geology, biology and agricultural chemistry in the 18th and 19th century. In the 20th century, it has evolved to an independent discipline which was manifested by the foundation of the International Society of Soil Science in Rome in 1924. Soil science originally focussed on pedogenetic processes but soil scientists also study the water and matter dynamics in the soil-plant-aquifer-atmosphere system and quantify loss of soil particles through erosion by wind and water, losses of solutes through drainage water, and gaseous losses. It is a multidisciplinary science which interlinks knowledge of the atmosphere, the biosphere, the lithosphere and the hydrosphere (Sumner, 2000; Lal, 2002; Benbi and Nieder, 2003).

Challenges for the 21st century

Severe problems facing humanity in the 21st century are a present world population of 6.1 billion, increasing by 1.3%/yr, food-insecurity and malnutrition in most of Africa and parts of South America and Asia, excess fertilization with nitrogen and phosphorus in many other parts of the world leading to pollution of freshwaters, eutrophication and acidification of terrestrial and coastal ecosystems, decreasing biodiversity. Mean annual temperature will increases between 1°C and 6°C by 2100, causing sea level to rise by 90 cm and changes in weather patterns (droughts, floods, storms). The global per capita arable land area of 0.23 ha will decrease to 0.14 ha in 2050, fresh water supply will decrease to the scarcity level in many countries and extreme forms of degradation will affect more than 300 million ha of agricultural land, particularly in countries where farmers cannot invest in soil restoration. Challenges directly related to soil science are given below, together with some priority research areas:

Soil erosion
- Analysis of the chain of processes between the driving forces of erosion and ecological and socio-economic effects;
- Influence of land use and climate change, management, desertification, savannah and forest fires and snow melt;
- Application of soil information and remote sensing for risk assessment on different scales;
- Development of new conservation and remediation methods.

Soil organic matter and biodiversity
- Definition of SOM in relation to soil functions and the potential to sequester C and N under contrasting environments;
- Development of standardized methods characterizing soil biodiversity;
- Effects of climate change and related land use and management changes
- Relationship between biodiversity and soil functioning;
- Use of different scales from whole organisms to the protein and the functional (mRNA) level;
- Identification of combined management practices to optimize SOM and soil biodiversity.

Excess fertilization
- Identification of driving forces on excess fertilization with N and P and quantification of their ecological and economic effects;
- Definition of environmentally friendly levels of livestock densities;
- Optimization of methods for adapting the N and P fertilization to the crop nutrient demand;
- Combination of mineral and organic fertilizers in view of optimum SOM conditions.

Soil contamination
- Identification and quantification of contamination sources (geogenic and anthropogenic);
- Improving methods for measurement of air-born contaminants;
- Investigation of the route of entry, the fate and the long-term behaviour and identification of potentially dangerous and new substances in the soil-plant-sediment-water system;

- Bioavailability of contaminants for humans, animals, plants and soil organisms;
- Risk assessment for outputs from soil;
- Improvement of techniques for remediation of contaminated soil.

Soil sealing
- Effect on the water and matter flow in urban, suburban and rural areas;
- Impacts on local, landscape and global level;
- Establishment of a nomenclature to be applied for regions or countries;
- Establishment of methods to survey sealing with respect to area quality and quantity.

Soil compaction
- Analyses of compaction effects on soil quality;
- Definition of soil conditions which are sensitive to compaction;
- Assessment of trends in agricultural machinery causing deep reaching compaction;
- Implementation of methods for predicting stress transmission and soil deformation;
- Development of management tools to reduce soil compaction.

▪ Soil alkalinization
- Assessment under different climate, soil management and irrigation water quality;
- Investigation of the factors which make a soil sensitive to salinization/ sodification;
- Influence of different water flow conditions (matrix and preferential flow) on alkalinization;
- Investigation of the (ir)reversibility of soil degradation processes caused by alkalinization;
- Identification of indicators for alkalinization and changes of soil structure and hydrology;
- Interrelationships between alkalinization and desertification and strategies for salt reclamation.

Conclusions
Problems will aggravate with the rapidly increasing world population unless adequate measures of control are taken. Therefore, multidisciplinary cooperation of soil scientists with geological, biological, physical, toxicological, hydrological, geographical, geo-information, engineering, social, economic and political sciences is essential. Policy makers are finally requested to develop rational land use and management policies including

anti-degradation measures. Several international documents are existing with respect to soil protection, e.g. the World Soil Charta of the FAO (1981), and the Agenda 21 (chapters 10 to 14) of the UN Conference in Rio de Janeiro (1992). The EU is currently developing a Thematic Strategy on Soil Protection as part of the 6th Environment Action Programme which is to be adopted in spring 2006 (European commission, 2004). However, as long as these texts are restricted to recommendation character, they will show limited success.

References

Benbi, D.K. and R. Nieder (eds.), 2003. Handbook of processes and modeling in the soil-plant system. Haworth Press, New York, pp. 762.

European Commission (eds. L. Van-Camp, B. Bujarrabal, A.R. Gentile, R.J.A. Jones, L. Monatanarella, C. Olazabal, S.K. Selvaradjou), 2004. Reports of the technical working groups established under the thematic strategy for soil protection, Volume I, Introduction and executive summary.

Lal, R. (ed.), 2002. Encyclopedia of soil science. Marcel Dekker, New York. Sumner, M.E. (ed.), 2000. Handbook of soil science. CRC Press, Boca Raton.

◆

The challenge of harnessing soil and water resources

Andrew D. Noble

IWMI-SEA, c/o WorldFish Centre, Jalan Batu Maung, Batu Maung, 11960 Bayan Lepas, Penang, Malaysia. E-mail a.noble@cgiar.org

> *We know more about the movement of the*
> *celestial bodies than about the soil underfoot*
> Leonardo da Vinci

The words of Leonardo da Vinci, although written in the 15th century, are still relevant today. Land and water are the central elements in the livelihoods of all people on earth, whether they inhabit rural areas or the mega cities of the 21st century. Humanity is dependent on these elements for food, livestock, clothes, industrial processes and shelter. In addition, we are dependent on these elements for environmental goods and services that are vital to our very existence.

If we accept that our very existence on this planet is tied to the extremely thin *skin*, called soil, which covers the unweathered and partially weathered geological formations of Earth's surface, and that this *skin* is effectively a fragile veneer, then the importance of managing and conserving this resource becomes paramount to our continued existence. Moreover, if we accept that soil and water are inextricably linked and that when considered in unison their impact is additive, then effective and sustainable management of these resources is paramount. Notwithstanding this, the critical link between these biophysical components is the social and economic attributes of our society.

In the face of the Millennium Development Goals (MDG), which has as its target to halve the proportion of poor and hungry by 2015, there will be a requirement to feed a further 900 million new persons and improve the dietary components of 400 million others. This will have to be achieved within the context of climate change and falling productivity of land based production systems.

The looming water scarcity crisis, declining productivity of land resources and changing demographic patterns globally, will limit our ability to enhance grain outputs at levels commensurate with demand unless innovation and investments are made in land and water resources. We can no longer increase agricultural output through lateral expansion of the industry without negative impacts on already stressed ecosystems. It is argued that productivity increases will require addressing degradation issues associated with current agro-ecosystems and improving the productivity of both 'blue' and 'green' water.

The challenges that we face as soil scientists in the 21st century are no different from those previously, but will have a somewhat different focus. It is argued that agricultural scientist will be faced with the task of growing more food, fibre and livestock on less water and declining total land area. The question is how will this be achieved?

Considerable emphasis has been placed on genetically modified crops and their introduction into current production systems as an enabling technology that will meet the food and fibre demands of the future. This is based on the indisputable successes achieved through the 'green revolution' and the accompanying package of technologies that supported this development. A key element in the success of the 'green revolution' was the introduction of affordable high analysis inorganic fertilizers, in particular urea and super phosphate. High analysis fertilizers formed the basic element in nutrient supply to genetically improved crop varieties and continue to be used ubiquitously by the agricultural industry with very little, if any, change to the basic mechanism of nutrient supply. There is a downside to the use of mobile high analysis chemical species, usually exhibited as degradation of soil (structural breakdown, acidity etc) and as waterway and aquifer pollution.

There is a need to re-evaluate this whole aspect of nutrient delivery to crops. The concept of applying fertilizers in a form that resists leaching and 'fixation', with the added bonus of effecting changes to fundamental soil properties thereby permanently increasing soil capacity to retain added nutrients, has been proposed and demonstrated (Gillman and Noble 2005). Whilst the supply of nutrients on hydrotalcite and bentonite platforms will be more expensive than conventional fertilizer applications, the proposed technology could initially be targeted at areas of known risk, such as light-textured soils in close proximity to water bodies, where regulation might not permit the use of soluble fertilizer (Gillman and Noble 2005). In addition, the supply of nutrients in a fully exchangeable form presents the opportunity to develop designer fertilizers to fit specific farmer requirements and environmental conditions. There is a need to develop innovative and affordable nutrient delivery platforms that reduce, if not eliminate, the potential negative off-site impacts, particularly for use in less developing countries where the level of regulation or technological sophistication has yet to be attained.

It is argued that significant opportunities exist in enhancing the productivity of what could be termed 'under performing' production systems. In a recently completed global survey of 286 projects where new technologies or practices have been implemented by individual farmers or communities in developing countries, there is clear evidence that significant gains in productivity can be achieved, particularly at the lower end of the yield spectrum (Fig. 1). What is encouraging is that new technology/knowledge was a key driver in achieving these productivity gains. Implicit in these productivity gains has been an enhancement in water productivity. There is broad agreement that future increases in water scarcity will turn water into a key, or the key, limiting factor in food production and livelihoods generation for the majority of people on earth. As demand for water increases from sectors of national economies other than agriculture, there will be less water diverted for the growing of food, fibre and livestock and hence a need to increase the productivity of water. It is in this arena that soil science can and should play a significant role.

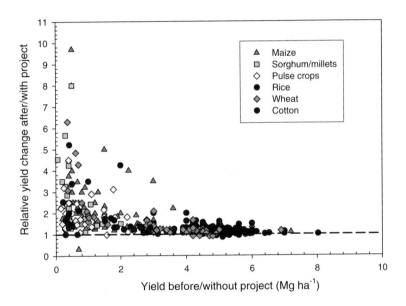

Fig. 1. Changes in the yields of agronomic crops with the adoption of new technologies and practices on a global basis. The data set is made up of 446 crop yields from 286 projects. Dashed line indicates no change in relative yield (Noble et al., 2006).

Improving the nutrient supplying and water holding capacity; access to stored soil water through addressing soil physical constraints; nutrient and water conservation methods; and the re-use of waste products from industry and mega cities as soil conditioners will all contribute to improving water use efficiency. It is argued that significant productivity gains can be achieved through the rehabilitation of degraded rainfed production systems and the rehabilitation of irrigated soils affected by salinity and sodicity.

The challenge for soil scientists as we move towards achieving the MDG will be to provide innovative solutions to addressing degraded agricultural production systems. The greatest increases in productivity will be achieved in those systems that are under performing that predominate in developing countries.

References
Gillman. G.P., and Noble, A.D., 2005. Environmentally manageable fertilizers: A new approach. Environmental Quality Management 15: 59-70.

Noble, A.D., Bossio, D., Penning de Vries, F. W. T., Pretty, J. Thiyagarajan, T. M., 2006. Intensifying agricultural sustainability – an analysis of impacts and drivers in the development of 'Bright Spots'. Research Report. Colombo, International Water Management Institute (in the press).

◆

Soil science in to the 21st century

Stephen Nortcliff

Department of Soil Science, University of Reading, Reading, RG6 6DW United Kingdom. E-mail: iuss@reading.ac.uk

When I began my career in soil science in the early 1970's the focus of much of soil science research was on the agricultural use of soils and how production could be maximised by soil management, focusing on fertiliser amendments and soil management. Whilst the focus was strongly on maintaining and increasing agricultural production there was awareness that this was achieved in some cases by damaging the soil. The Strutt Report of 1970 entitled 'Modern Farming and the Soil' (MAFF, 1970) was a response to a series of difficult UK harvests in the 1960s and a levelling off of the production curve. This report highlighted structural damage to soil and associated decreases in productivity if cultivation was poorly timed and occurred when the soil was wet. It also noted that soils were more susceptible, particularly in eastern England, where soil organic matter levels had been allowed to decline.

For much of the next 10-15 years my research within Europe and the tropics focused on improving or maintaining agricultural production, often in the tropics through bringing previously unused land in to agricultural production. During this period relatively little mention was made of the need to consider soil as part of the environmental system, and sustainability concerns were on maintaining yield not the soil system. How things have changed as we have moved in to the 21st Century! Whilst maintaining agricultural production is still important the emphasis now is on the sustainable use of soils and limiting or removing the negative effects on other environmental components. This change has been coupled with an increased awareness within the political sphere of the importance of soils in relation to other environmental systems, indeed the soil is recognised by many to have a key role lying at the interface between the atmosphere, biosphere, lithosphere and hydrosphere. The soil may be only a few centimetres or at most metres thick at the earth's surface, but it is now recognised as having a pivotal role in how aspects of the global environmental system operate. Within Europe this importance was recognised in 2002 when the European Commission launched its document 'Towards a Thematic Strategy for Soil Protection' (Commission of European Communities, 2002). This initiative has been matched by many national strategies for soil protection within European Member States. The European Commission document and the subsequent programme to identify the priority concerns and actions for soil protection have set the theme for the immediate and possibly the longer term future of soil science within Europe. The document emphasised that there must be a broader consideration of soil's role in the environment; five broad but vital soil functions were identified:

- Food and other biomass production
- Storing, filtering and transformations
- Habitat and gene pool
- Physical and cultural environment for mankind
- Source of raw materials

Whilst food and biomass production is included there is a much wider coverage than had been generally recognised previously. Because of this wide range of functions, it is essential that soil condition was maintained if sustainability is to be achieved. In addition it was stated that soils were under threat from a range of human activities which were undermining soil's long term availability and viability. They listed the most significant threats as:

- Erosion
- Decline in organic matter
- Contamination
- Soil sealing
- Compaction
- Decline in biodiversity
- Salinisation
- Floods and landslides

Within much of Western Europe these have become the foci for future developments in soil science. Coupled with the shift from production oriented to a much broader environmental perspective this is the way forward for soil science. Globally the increasingly urbanized population provides a major focus for soil science. Urban expansion frequently seals soil, and in most cases removes it from any potential future use. It is essential that soil scientists are involved in sustaining the use of soils within these urbanization processes. Sustainable use will involve avoiding sealing wherever possible, but also seeking to identify local uses of soils removed during the construction processes. Relatively few soil scientists have been actively involved in this area, but it is one where our knowledge of the nature of soil and how it behaves under a range of conditions is essential if both the short and long term environmental impacts of the urbanization process are to be reduced.

On a global scale soil scientists must become more actively involved in environmental issues. For example, whilst the importance of the soil carbon pool in global carbon budgets is now widely recognized, soil scientists must continue to emphasize this importance and ensure that we have science-based strategies to prevent further declines in the magnitude of this pool, particularly in the context of changing environmental conditions, and strategies to encourage increases in the soil carbon pool. Linked to this are concerns about possible declines in the soil's biodiversity. Whilst the concerns are real, we still do not fully understand many of the soil biological processes nor do we understand the interactions and dynamics of the wide range of organisms found in the soil. Given the importance of soil biodiversity both in terms of soil carbon pools and budgets and in terms of linkages with broader environmental biodiversity, it is essential that we achieve a fuller understanding of the processes and also identify which organisms can be used as robust indicators of the changes in soil biodiversity which will influence other parts of the soil system and beyond.

For many years soil was not a major political issue, but it changed in the 21st century. The European Commission following its 'Thematic Strategy for Soil Protection' appears to be moving towards a Directive to guide soil management and protection; within the United Kingdom the 'Soil Action Plan for England, 2004-2006' was launched (DEFRA, 2004). Soil scientists have been involved in the development of these legislative frameworks, but we should consider developing broader international approaches. Hannam and Boer (2002; 2004) have produced some preliminary guidance on how we might move towards an 'International Protocol for Soil Protection' or possibly an 'International Convention for Soil Protection'. Whilst either of these will involve many more groups than soil scientists, it is essential that we as soil scientists are fully involved in their development.

Soil is now recognized as a key environmental component which can be easily abused and lost. It is recognized as a finite resource. Soil scientists in the 21st century must be ready and able to provide information to other scientists and those setting the political agenda on how to avoid the abuse of soil and how to optimize the role of soils in broader environmental contexts.

References

Commission of the European Communities, 2002. Communication 'Towards a thematic strategy for soil protection', Brussels.

DEFRA, 2004. Soil action plan for England- 2004-2006, London

Hannam, I. and Boer, B., 2002. Legal and institutional framework for sustainable soil use: A preliminary report. IUCN environmental policy and law paper No. 45. IUCN, Gland.

Hannam, I. and Boer, B., 2002. Drafting legislation for sustainable soils: A guide. IUCN Environmental Policy and Law paper No. 52. IUCN, Gland.

MAFF, 1970. Modern farming and the soil, HMSO, London

◆

Soil science: multiple scales and multiple opportunities

Gary W. Petersen

Department of Crop and Soil Sciences, The Pennsylvania State University, University Park, PA 16802, USA. E-mail gwp2@psu.edu

In the past, soil science has served a strong production focus in agriculture with little attention to the soil processes that maintain the functioning of agroecosystems.   Much of the focus in pedology has been on the development of soil taxonomic systems. As we look into the future there are a number of questions that need to be asked by soil scientists. Some of these questions might be:

- What should we do to maintain our relevance within the scientific community and within society in general?
- How do we develop strategies for managing both spatial and temporal soil changes?
- How do we do integrative science at landscape and watershed levels?
- What can we do to increase the visibility of soil science?

Pedologists have additional concerns such as how to develop approaches for characterizing, monitoring, predicting, and managing soil changes and what tools are required to make suitable predictions about soil and landscape conditions and sustainable land use.

The future of soil science is both exciting and challenging. We have never had as many issues for soil scientists to address or as many opportunities for them to investigate as we have in today's society. We are also fortunate because we have a broad array of new technologies available to the soil science community. Some of these technologies include remote sensing and geospatial information systems. For the first time in history we have technologies for global data collections at multiple scales. Combining these technologies with digital databases along with their incorporation into geospatial models should afford many opportunities to help us understand soil ecosystems and associated problems.

There are many issues facing society today that are related either directly or indirectly to soil science. Some of these issues cut across many different scales and political levels and they have been summarized in the figure on the next page.

Scale Issues: Activities & Impacts

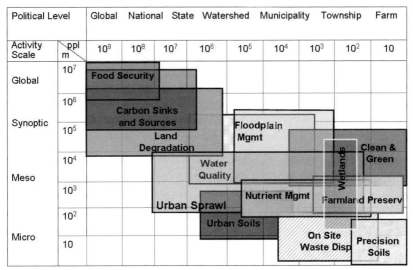

Political Level		Global	National	State	Watershed	Municipality	Township	Farm
Activity Scale	ppl / m	10^9	10^8	10^7	10^6	10^5	10^4	10^3	10^2	10

In the future we need to focus on the critical role of soil in the ecosystem and its function in the landscape. The challenges will be to:

- Abandon our current narrow perspective and to become involved in systems-level analysis;
- Start integrating our skills to generate landscape-scale solutions over multiple temporal and spatial scales;
- Refocus our efforts to educate the next generation of students.

One of our most important challenges will be that of student education. This should involve a restructuring of student curricula including basic soil courses, integrative courses at the landscape level, information technology and analysis techniques, business courses, social awareness courses and experiences, and soil application courses and internships. Students must be given a global perspective and emphasis must be placed on improving their communication skills.

In summary, the future of soil science has never been brighter or more exciting than it is today. However, one of the keys to the future will be to develop the next generation of soil scientists. It will be a difficult task and I hope everyone is up to the challenge.

♦

Future of soil science

Ildefonso Pla Sentís
Departament de Medi Ambient i Ciències del Sòl Universitat, de Lleida Av. Alcalde Rovira Roure 191, 25198 Lleida. Spain. E-mail ipla@macs.udl.es

Soil is fundamental to the needs of man life, because it provides most of our basic needs and plays a central role in determining the quality of our environment, but this is not well appreciated by most of the population. In the future, the role of soils and soil cover in some crucial aspects for man's life like food production, the hydrological cycle, and air composition will further increase. Therefore, more soil information of good quality will be required for adequate decisions about land use and management. The main and final goal of soil science will continue to be the evaluation and prediction of the behaviour of soils in time and space, under a wide range of agricultural and non agricultural land uses, in relation to crop production, water supply and environment quality. At present, most of the major decisions about agriculture and environment, and in general about world development, are usually made without taking into consideration the prominent role of soil science.

Present situation

The rapid increase in population, with higher food and water demands, is causing more human influences on soils, both through the expansion and intensification of agricultural activities and the growth of number and size of populated areas. Frequently, it leads to widespread land and soil degradation, and increased production of farming, domestic and industrial wastes. The main consequences are a decrease in the reserves of arable lands, increasing agricultural developments in new lands with unfavourable climate and relief conditions. There is a decrease in available good quality water for agriculture, urban and industrial needs, and a decrease in biological diversity.

These problems may lead to dramatic environmental, social and economic consequences that in the poorer developing regions are manifested trough decreased crop productivity, increased poverty and migration. There are also increased risks and problems of desertification, flooding, landslides, sedimentation, etc. The shrinkage of water resources of good quality is limiting the development of irrigated agriculture, and is increasing the risks of salinization and contamination of soils. It is also worth to mention the contribution of changes in soil cover and soil degradation to global climate changes. The increased degradation of soils and their consequences may be attributed to the lack of awareness by most of the human society, and of the institutions where decisions of land use and management planning are taken, about the capital role and functions of soils for man life.

Although contributions of soil science have benefited humankind by increasing agricultural food production and enhancing the environmental quality, at present there is a dangerous general slowdown on those trends. Concurrently, there has been a decrease in resources dedicated to field oriented soil science studies, and much of the present research in soil science is dedicated to isolated aspects, not covering integral problems, due to limitations of time and funds, to the difficulties of interdisciplinary cooperation, and to the compulsion of publishing papers quickly. At the same time, there has been an increased tendency to rely on qualitative data and concepts, based on expert judgements, like indices of soil quality, with a very limited accuracy, insufficient for developing adequate policies for land use and management. Moreover, frequently land use planning is being based on empirical approaches coming from professionals with scarce formation in soil science.

Planning land use and management requires input data which is site specific, but in many cases the kind of required information is not available. One of the difficulties found in the assessment of soil conditions related to the performance of soils under different land use and management, and climate change, based on already existing data, is that most of the previously made soil surveys provided static information, while for soil functions there are necessary more dynamic soil parameters. Modelling is extensively used as a tool to integrate information, and to avoid measurements and field experiments for every soil and condition. Modelling is not a substitute for experimentation and models need input parameters of good quality, obtained not only in laboratory tests, but also under controlled field conditions. These studies are not common because they are time consuming, costly and difficult to finish in a publication fulfilling the requirements of soil science journals. Therefore, they are substituted in many cases by empirical approaches, or the use of data that are already available or easier to obtain, empirically deducing, by the use of pedotransfer functions, of properties and processes required for modelling. Much of the accepted and used methodology and instruments for evaluating parameters of soils in the laboratory do not give data which correspond to real, or even approximate, values under field conditions. In general, the progress in developing models and processing systems of information have been much faster than in the development and use of methodologies and equipment to get the adequate field information to feed them.

Challenges for the future

In general the future developments in soil science research must be directed to a better understanding of the processes and reactions in soils related with crop production, chemical recycling and water balance, over a range of spatial and temporal scales. Of particular importance will be the improved identification and description of important dynamic processes in soils critical for the supply of water and nutrients for plant growth and for soil degradation, as affected by external temporal factors like climate. This has to be followed by the development of simplified simulation models to find the best combination of management practices, integrating selected critical parameters of soils, crops and climate, for a more efficient and economical use of soil water and energy addressed to increased crop production, overcoming depletion and minimizing risks of soil, water and environmental degradation, including risks of natural disasters like flooding and landslides.

In order to assure the prominence that soil science should have in the future World development there will be necessary to improve the education and awareness of population at all levels about the relevant functions of soils for the life of mankind. There are also required an improvement and a reorientation in the training in soil science addressed to soil scientists and other professionals involved in the design and planning of land use and management, with a more holistic approach, reinforcement of hydrological aspects and a better integration of theory and field work. To guarantee an interdisciplinary approach there would be necessary an increased cooperation among soil scientists and scientists of related disciplines, and among institutions involved in research and application of soil and land use and management.

◆

Future of soil science: tackle the big issues

David S. Powlson
Agriculture and Environment Division, Rothamsted Research, Harpenden, Herts. AL5 2JQ, United Kingdom. E-mail david.powlson@bbsrc.ac.uk

Despite a widespread anti-science trend, at least in Europe, there is a genuine concern about the environment among many citizens worldwide. It is logical, and I think essential, for soil scientists to be active in addressing the issues fuelling this concern. This is both an honest application of our skills and a sensible strategy to attract funding and students. Although there will be different prioritisations in different regions of the world, the "big issues" will surely include:

- Climate change, especially its mitigation or exacerbation through soil processes;
- Pathways and impacts of pollutants at local and global scale;
- Growing sufficient food, especially in the face of water shortage;
- Nutrient enrichment and other human impacts on the functioning of semi-natural ecosystems.

Tackling these subjects will inevitably require increased collaboration with colleagues in other disciplines (natural and social sciences) – there are few major issues that can be understood (still less solved) using expertise from a single viewpoint. Meaningful engagement with decision makers, regulators and fellow citizens will be an increasingly essential element of our jobs. We need to hear their perspectives, explain and interpret the role of soils in ecosystem functions of importance to humans, and demonstrate that we can effectively assist in understanding, avoiding and solving problems. This will not always be a populist strategy – sometimes it will mean challenging simplistic views often promulgated by pressure groups or disagreeing with commercial interests or government policies.

Soils - pure or applied science?

I submit that soil science is a predominantly applied subject. By this I mean that the *main* rationale for studying soils is functional: humans either want to *use* soils or recognise that they are *affected by them*. Soil *use* is obvious in agriculture and land-based industries, whether biologically based (growing plants) or engineering based (construction, mineral extraction, water supply). It is also clear for recreational uses of land, whether sports fields or hiking. But even environmental concerns are mainly anthropocentric – we wish the environment to function well by providing clean water and air, a reasonably predictable climate and natural habitats that we value for aesthetic or cultural reasons. By positioning our discipline centrally in the applied science arena we can compete for funding more effectively than by using a mainly "pure" science argument. This does not imply an empirical approach - to address applied questions a fundamental understanding of underlying processes is normally essential. But it is far easier to justify resources for appropriate fundamental studies if the applied case for studying soil has already been made and accepted.

Despite arguing for a functional approach, my experience is that soil research can reveal tantalising fundamental insights. For example, the strong stabilisation of organic matter in soil and the astonishing survival and diversity of microbes under adverse conditions may well shed light on the origins of life – there are fewer more fundamental issues! Thus, some aspects of soil science can, and should, be fully justified alongside any "pure" science; but cannot be the *main* way of securing sufficient funding for the discipline.

A resurgence of soil science to serve agriculture?
Over-production of food in the EU and North America, and the perception by urban citizens of agriculture as a polluting activity, has precipitated cuts in agricultural research. I suggest that this trend will change as the needs of 8-10 billion people later this century become clear in a globally connected world. This will be driven by political and business considerations as much as humanitarian concerns. To provide food, fibre, fuel and livelihoods in the light of land scarcity, soil degradation, water shortages, etc. (probably worsened by climate change) will call for innovative applications of current knowledge and research to develop a diverse range of novel approaches. New technologies and developments from traditional practices will both be needed. Soil scientists should be foundational members of the teams addressing these challenges. Topics will include:

- Avoiding and remediating salinity;
- Using limited water and nutrients more efficiently;
- Controlling soil erosion;
- Minimising environmental damage whilst achieving desired production;
- Efficient recycling of manures and other wastes for crop production and energy.

The resurgence in global agricultural research could be a well-coordinated effort to maximise production in regions of greatest potential and achieve at least *some* sustainable production in unpromising situations, whilst taking full account of environmental interactions. Unfortunately current actions, including forest clearance in South America, wasteful increases in agrochemical use in Asia, and inefficient water use almost everywhere, suggest it will include remediating problems caused by poorly-planned agricultural intensification.

Methods, models, mapping and monitoring

A wealth of new methods is becoming available – some potential tools for research on the details of soil functioning (e.g. various spectroscopies, molecular biology, imaging) have the power to initiate totally new areas of enquiry. Others are applicable to the collection and manipulation of soil data at a range of scales from field to global (e.g. proxy analyses, remote sensing, modelling) and thus valuable for monitoring, management and policy development. It is essential that some soil scientists are at the forefront of exploring new methodologies, in collaboration with appropriate specialist. But it is equally important that they, or other soil scientists, are active in testing the new approaches under realistic conditions and then *applying* them to significant questions, so they become valuable tools rather than minority art forms.

Teaching soil science

If there are to be soils scientists in the future it is essential to communicate the fascination of soils and their importance for humanity to school students and, most strategically, to teachers. At the University level, the decline in numbers of departments concentrating purely on soil science is not necessarily negative. Embedding of soil science in broadly based departments can lead to extra students receiving some teaching on soils. But there is also a need for soil science specialists, with implications for "critical mass" of expertise. The trend to deliver specialist training at post-graduate level may be beneficial, attracting students with varied backgrounds. For all students, teaching should obviously be rigorous and challenging. But for those teaching the broader groups I would encourage a rigorous yet "functional" approach, helping students to see what soils *do* within managed or natural ecosystems and equipping them to make management decisions. Most of all make it interesting! Although classification is important, those difficult words can wait until later.

♦

Maintaining the soil ecosystems of the future

D.L.N. Rao

Indian Institute of Soil Science, Bhopal-462 038, Madhya Pradesh, India. E-mail dlnrao@iiss.ernet.in

> *Manuring profiteth more than the ploughing: and when the land is weeded, guarding it profiteth more than irrigation.*
> Tiruvalluvar, Tamil poet-philosopher
> of ancient India, 2000 yrs BP

Soil ecosystems remain firmly at the foundations of human life support systems. They are the least understood among the natural ecosystems and increasingly among the most degraded. Soil erosion, loss of soil organic matter and nutrient depletion are among the leading contributors to impaired soil health, reduced crop yields and poverty in developing world. Global warming will further exacerbate the problem. Not surprisingly therefore, soil health tops a list of priorities of the UN Millennium Goal Project's hunger task force. Green revolution based on high yielding crop varieties, chemical fertilizers and pesticides, addressed the yield and poverty issues, but brought new concerns on soil health sustainability. The effects of physical and chemical degradation of soils are quite obvious, but biological degradation due to the loss of specific soil organic matter fractions and the autochthonous biotic communities dependent upon them is insidious.

The ancient wisdom and indigenous technical knowledge about benefits of manuring, reduced tillage, conservation farming and other practices abandoned somewhere on the way, need to be re-learnt to preserve this diversity. There is scientific evidence now that such ecologically benign practices promote floral and faunal diversity, optimize nutrient cycling, maximize input use efficiency, create sinks for CO_2 and other GHG's, and leave the biological control mechanisms intact whilst also achieving high yields. An increase of one tonne of organic carbon pool of degraded cropland soils may increase crop yields by 20-40 kg ha^{-1} for wheat and 10-20 kg ha^{-1} for maize (Lal, 2004). Soil organic matter levels must thus be restored, enhanced and improved. The connection between soil carbon sequestration, improved soil health and yields, world food security and poverty alleviation is thus obvious and is at the heart of soil scientists' vision of how science can be delivered to the world's poor.

Soil is the most complicated biomaterial on the planet. A changed perception of soils from an exclusive focus as substrate for food production to its ecological and biodiversity potential has firmly emerged. Microbes are the basis of the biosphere; a staggering 5×10^{31} cells exist, weighing 50 quadrillion metric tones, constituting about 60% of the total biomass. It is difficult to overstate their importance; the soil-microbe complex is vital because of the services it provides for agriculture, waste management and the water industry, and the natural and semi-natural environments. They breakdown most of the 45,000 or so chemical compounds that humans use in daily life. With molecular techniques, the incredible diversity of soil microorganisms is finally being unravelled. More than 90% of the planet's genetic biodiversity is resident in soils but less than 1% of the microorganisms have been cultured and studied. The genotypic diversity in all the Protists groups is far more than the combined diversity of plant, animal or fungal kingdom. This enormous gene reserve in soils will be exploited in future industry and pharmaceutics, with diverse benefits of far greater value.

Understanding the structure-function relation of microbial communities has been difficult. A greater understanding of the functional bridges between the physics and biology of soils will be required. Environmental genomics will be crucial in exploring microbial diversity and its functional significance. Complex interactions between plants and consortia of microbes would extend beyond those resisting pathogens and scavenging nutrients and would help improve drought resistance and salt tolerance of plants and have other growth-promoting activities. Mycorrhiza help plants to tolerate stress through extensive networks of mycelia, sometime extending up to 20,000 km in one cubic metre of soil. Understanding and managing soil microbial ecology will have major benefits for stressed agricultural systems and will also help determine optimal tradeoffs while using heavy doses of fertilizers and pesticides such that benefits of use outweigh the disruptions caused. There would be greater focus on soil faunal activities whose neglect has been a matter of great concern. Integrated farming systems using legume BNF, composts, green manures, microbial inoculants (biofertilizers), biopesticides, etc. would be increasingly used along with judicious use of irrigation water in all production systems. Exploring the extent of microbial impacts on climate change and the effects of climate change on microbes would be a major scientific challenge.

Soil science and soil scientists have thrived because of inter-disciplinary co-operation and shown how soils frequently play roles as the keystone of environmental systems, both natural and managed, and contributed significantly to local, regional and global environmental management. Soil scientists have this rare attribute because their expertise is based both in the laboratory and in the field. In the future they will play a major role in addressing the complex nature of land use, climate change impacts on soils and agriculture, environmental, and biodiversity challenges mentioned previously. Therefore re-fashioning soil science education by greater re-integration of the basic disciplines is a virtual imperative. Soil scientists should benefit from the best of both- basic sciences coupled with practical skills- so as to create an army of diverse specialists, a mosaic, which would remove the present uniform and redundant training they receive (Rao, 2004). As Stephen Nortcliff noted (Personal communication, 2005) "Soil science should not be defended by erecting barriers to others, but by showing the strength and diversity of our knowledge and the substantial contributions we are able to make together with scientists of other disciplines". Experts in ecology, biosystematics, molecular biology, biochemistry, imaging sciences, nanotechnology etc. have to be engaged in the new endeavours. There are now uncommon opportunities for ensuring efficient land care, clean environment and better life; we should put our best efforts in maintaining this vital, non-renewable resource in a pristine state for future ecological security. Then only, would soil scientists have come `good' and an increasingly ecology conscious society, sees and appreciates the value of soil scientists and the work we do. Let us face the future with optimism.

References

Lal, R., 2004. Soil carbon sequestration impacts on global climate change and food security. Science 304: 1623-1627.

Rao D.L.N., 2004. Paradigms in Soil Science. Indian Society Soil Science Newsletter 17: 1-2.

♦

The future of soil science in less developed countries

Abdul Rashid

National Agricultural Research Center, Park Road, Islamabad-45500, Pakistan.
Email abdul.rashid@comsats.net.pk

Soils sustain life – by performing a number of vital functions in the ecosystem, in addition to supporting agricultural production. However, historically, soils have been appreciated, and managed, for food and fibre production only – for sustaining life on this planet earth. Within the arena of agricultural sciences, soil science predominantly pertains to the study (and management) of soil from the view point of plant growth. No doubt, the immediate need and challenge in developing countries remains food security, however with increased need and awareness in the recent times, environmental issues have come to occupy a centre stage in soil science – as is true elsewhere around the world. The role of soils in protecting the environment can not be over emphasized when we consider how it controls geochemistry of pollutants by decomposing wastes, regulating the flow of water and filtering the contaminants.

Due to over-exploitation and inappropriate land use in less developed countries of the world, to cope with increased food and fibre requirements of their fast growing populations, various soil degradation processes have deteriorated, and are continuously deteriorating, the soil resource base. Soil can not remain a mute spectator to all the abuses heaped on it; neither soil possesses infinite resilience to withstand an ever increasing pressure put on it, by way of enhanced biomass production and increased pollution load. As climatic conditions limit the rehabilitative physical, chemical and biological processes, soil degradation is reflected as a loss in farm productivity, and, in many situations, a threat to agricultural production systems. Consequently, even in well endowed irrigated areas of many less developed countries, the production systems are showing signs of fatigue. On the top of this, pollution of soil and surface water bodies by indiscriminate use of municipal and industrial wastes in the city suburbs, and by pesticide and nutrient movement down the soil profile – in high-input cropping systems – is a fact of life.

As natural resources, including soil, in most of the less developed countries have degraded over the past few decades, the crucial challenge for soil scientists is to sustain the soil resource base by containing and, even reversing the soil degradation processes. The real challenge in less developed countries is to rejuvenate the soil resources for meeting ever-increasing food and fibre demands of fast increasing populations, while protecting the environment. For attaining food security, we need to strive for enhancing crop yields, and attain farm-level yields closer to the genetic potential. This is achievable, but only by science-based agriculture. Thus, soil scientists need to gear-up in terms of highly trained manpower, adequate research and development facilities, and matching resources.

While there is very limited possibility of lateral expansion in the cultivated area – primarily because of water scarcity, prime agricultural lands in the city suburbs are being brought under concrete structures – a situation indicative of our neglect of proper land-use planning. As soil development takes geological time periods, it is a non-renewable natural resource. We are appreciative of the fact that agricultural production can not be sustained without sustaining the natural resource base. Therefore, we are left with the only choice of conserving the precious soil resource base and improving its productivity — by adopting eco-friendly soil management practices. This can be accomplished, but only by applying science-based precise techniques to understand soil processes. Thus, soil scientists ought to address sustainability issues pertaining to agricultural productivity as well as the environment. However, because of extreme complexity and enormous variability within soils, the task of managing soil resources in a sustainable manner is a great challenge, indeed. The soil has to be managed within the framework of the biosphere, of which soil is an integral part. Therefore, the future efforts of soil management call for the integration of a host of related scientific disciplines directly or indirectly involved in the study of natural resources.

The environmental issues can only be addressed by gaining a better understanding of the physical, chemical, and biological processes. Currently, the requisite expertise and/or infrastructure in many less developed countries of the world, I am afraid, is inadequate. As these endeavours call for a matching human resource development and heavy investments in creation of the requisite research facilities, relevant decision makers must attach appropriate priorities by allocating adequate resources for the purpose.

Despite an ever-increasing importance of soil science for understanding and resolving increasingly complex issues pertaining to crop productivity and environmental protection, however, soil science remains a relatively under-developed science – as, unlike plants for example, soils lack a true universal classification system and, hence, nomenclature. Soil science is dynamic, and will remain so, because of extreme complexity and variability of the soils, and our limited understanding – which, for sure, will improve with persistent efforts. In recent times, sciences, including soil science, have become highly specialized; and we are heading for splendid isolation. While specialization is a positive omen for the progress of soil science, simultaneously we are getting isolated from ground realities. Like any other science, soil science should strive for serving humanity. For serving the cause of humanity, however, integration of knowledge is crucial. Therefore, we ought to impart broad-based training to the current and future soil scientists. While some present-day university professors – in developed countries of the world – are inclined for granting doctoral degree based entirely on laboratory/greenhouse and/or computer research, I remain highly appreciative of professors who do not grant this highest university degree without 'roughing out the student in the field'. Therefore, I would strongly emphasize for imparting adequate realization of broad-based agricultural ground realities to the future soil scientists.

Let us ponder as to what 'Soil Science' is expected to do in the present and in the future context. I understand that in future soil scientists will be called upon to answer more complex questions and that too in a precise manner. Thus, the road ahead is full of challenges and opportunities for soil scientists. The crucial question is "Are we prepared to face these challenges and avail the opportunities"?

In short, I foresee a crucial role of soil science in the future food security and wellbeing of the mankind – particularly in less developed countries of the world.

♦

International agricultural research: soil science at the crossroads

John Ryan
International Center for Agricultural Research in the Dry Areas (ICARDA), P.O., Box 5466, Aleppo, Syria. E-mail j.ryan@cgiar.org

The capacity of soil to sustain life and supply mankind with adequate food and fibre has historically been related to its fertility, or reserve of essential plant nutrients, as well as water from rainfall or from irrigation. Indeed, civilizations developed and flourished on areas of land with well-watered and fertile soils. Fertility of the world's soils enabled the global population to expand exponentially until the 19th century, at which time demand for food appeared to outstrip the earth's capacity to supply it, giving rise to the dire predictions of Malthus. The development of the chemical, fertilizer industry, and the widespread use of nitrogen, phosphorus, and potassium enabled the world to make a sustained quantum leap in food production throughout the 20th century, introducing a renewed sense of complacency as far as food security was concerned. The parallel development in the agricultural sciences, notably related to soils and crop nutrition, played a major role in eliminating nutrient deficiencies as crop growth constraints, as well as improving fertilizer- use efficiency and crop quality.

The latter part of the 20th century saw a glaring disparity emerge, with food sufficiency – indeed surpluses – in the developed world and famine and associated civil strife in several populous and ever-expanding developing countries. With limited possibilities for land expansion and with erosion and degradation posed an increasing threat to the soil resource base, the only solution was to stimulate applied soil-crop research and apply modern technologies to conditions in food-deficit countries. Thus, the need for, and genesis of, the international agricultural research systems.

The global Consultative Group on Agricultural Research or CGIAR was founded in 1971 based on existing international centres, notably in Morocco and Nigeria. The Centres were subsequently to expand in number and consolidate; currently there are 15 centres worldwide that deal with specific commodities (e.g., cereals, rice, animals), agroecosystems (drylands, agro-forestry, fisheries, biodiversity), and policies; some with a global mandate, other a regional one. Their broad objectives are to alleviate poverty through applied research, as well as protecting the environment and preserving biodiversity. The unique feature of such centres was their collaborative approach with national agricultural research systems in their mandate regions and with advanced institutions worldwide.

The CG centres, in essence, were built on the "Green Revolution" of the 1970s which embodied improved crop varieties and chemical fertilizer use. Thus, the element of nutrient constraints, supply and use featured largely in the applied research agenda of most centres. Notable achievements were made in nitrogen use in flooded rice production at the International Rice Research Institute (IRRI) in the Philippines; identification and amelioration of the suite of nutrient problems (deficiencies, toxicities), associated with acid tropical soils, notably in terms of phosphorus, at the International Center for Tropical Agriculture (CIAT), elucidation of N and P dynamics in dryland cropping systems at the International Center for Agricultural Research in the Dry Areas (ICARDA), including C carbon sequestration, micronutrients in calcareous soils, and nutrients in waste-water for irrigation, and water/nutrient use efficiency. Similarly, soil-related research was a major component of the work of the International Institute for Tropical Agriculture (IITA) in Nigeria, with a strong emphasis on erosion and soil degradation, while the nutrient component of the program of the International Center for Research in the Semi-Arid Tropics (ICRISAT) in India was integrated with water-use efficiency. Though primarily known for its crop breeding program for wheat and maize, the International Center for the Improvement of Wheat and Maize (CIMMYT) in Mexico has dealt with nutrients such as P and mycorhiza in cropping systems. Regardless of the crop or the environment, the common theme of all CG centre soil–related research was efficiency in production and resource sustainability, all with the ultimate goal of helping people.

Now, at the onset of the new millennium, the pace of change in the world has quickened; globalization, free trade and mass communication are factors in driving this change. As with all organizations, the CG centres are not immune to developments in the broader world. Notwithstanding the success of soil science in solving food production in developing countries, same intractable obstacles remain, especially in Africa where per capita food production and land use per capita has precariously declined. Obstacles in transferring soil-related technologies, especially for soil erosion control and fertilizer use, have to be seen in the context of wider constraints in terms of infrastructure and transport, credit systems and markets, and education an extension.

Major threats to the future of CG centres, which are largely funded by public money, will come from diversion of donor funding away from agriculture to areas such as health and education. Even when funding is relatively secure, there has been a shift in emphasis from core funding to donor – directed funding of more glamorous areas of research such as biotechnology. So far, there is little indication of biotechnology being a panacea for the developed world. The erroneous widely-held public perception that chemical fertilizers are harmful to the environment is a

Trojan-horse as far as developing countries are concerned. Well-fed industrialized countries with stagnant or declining populations may have the luxury of such notions, however valid they may be for their conditions, but, as crop yields are largely dependent on chemical fertilizers, developed countries cannot - and should not - be lulled into the mistaken belief that they can get by without the use of fertilizers. While organic agriculture has a niche role in the West, it cannot have any real impacts in developing countries. Soil nutrient research has shifted in the direction of human nutrition, mainstream soil research has, of necessity, to evolve with changing from practices, new crop varieties with higher nutrient needs, cropping intensification, and irrigation systems. Soil science must accommodate the twin objectives of producing food and ensuring the protecting the environment to ensure future capacity to produce food and fibre.

Soil science and related crop nutrition research has contributed greatly to the world. We should not let it now be a victim of its own success. The capacity to produce food cannot be taken for granted. Soil scientists as a body must communicate better to let the world's largely urban society what it has done and what it needs to do to ensure that future generations are well fed.

The CG centres of the future will need to attract dedicated highly trained and motivated scientists with clear perceptions of what concrete steps are needed to bring science to the poor. Re-inventing the wheel, woolly philosophy, or empty slogans will not prevent people from going to bed hungry. Without the realism and dedication of visionaries of international soil-crop scientists such as Norman Borlaug, Neil Brady, Pedro Sanchez, and Rattan Lal, the future of soil-crop research in the CG system cannot be guaranteed.

♦

Future of soil science

J.S. Samra

Indian Council of Agricultural Research, Krishi Anusandhan Bhawan-II, Pusa, New Delhi 110 012, India. Email jssamra2001@yahoo.com

Agricultural gross domestic product in most of the Asian countries is anything between 20 to 90% of the total and constitutes a major source of livelihood, income, employment and environmental securities. This situation is likely to compound because of slow progress in industrialization, very high demographic growth, excessive rate of urbanization and change in living styles/standards. In India per capita land availability has declined from 0.91 ha in 1951 to 0.35 ha in 2000 and is expected to go down further to 0.19 ha in 2050. Integrated management of soil, water, biodiversity and inputs qualities is becoming essential for realizing phyto-, bio- and geo- standards of globalised trade. Net availability of utilizable water is projected to decline from 2133 m^3 per person in 1996, to 1289 m^3 per person by 2050 and similar are the trends in China, Pakistan and other countries in Asia. Recycling of domestic and industrial effluents and geo-genic poor qualities waters will become major challenge of resources contaminations, sanitary and phyto-sanitary compliances.

Global warming, excessive melting of glaciers in the Himalayas, rise in sea level and significant changes in the frequency of extreme events like floods, droughts, cold waves, heat waves, cyclones and tsunamis has been authenticated by precisely analyzed data and several collateral evidences. Excessive erosion of highlands, submergence of some islands, highly populated coastal belts and relocation of human settlements to other agro-ecologies is a tremendous socio-economic responsibility of global warming impacts on land resources. Since natural resources like soil, water, bio-diversity and weather are the backbone of food, feed, nutritional and environment, their conservation, preservation and utilization will be a futuristic R&D flagship. The management portfolio of natural sciences is expected to be an intensive interplay of knowledge explosion, demographic growth, bio- and nano-technological opportunities of the developing world.

It is evident from the above scenarios that soil has to act as an inelastic source of livelihood, genomic wealth (like Bt genes) and environmental sink for assimilating anthropogenic solid wastes, domestic sewage, industrial effluents and other contaminants.

Since per capita availability of land resources is going to decline in the Asian region, the only alternative to sustain excessive demographic rate will be to enhance productivity of basic resources and inputs per unit area and time. Soil management is going to be highly capital inputs, energy intensive and knowledge based. Factor productivity of the Indo Gangetic plains with an overall productivity of 10 tons per ha/year of rice and wheat is already stagnating, deficiencies of nutrients are multiplying and cost competitiveness declining. The other possibility is to improve cropping intensity or relay cropping for maximizing employment, income, and production opportunities. These compulsions are so vital that the farmers of the Indo-Gangetic plains and China are burning rice residues and practicing zero tillage to seed/sow next crop since they cannot afford a few days for cultivation and incorporation of the residues. Incomplete burning of crop residues with high moisture contents generates carbon particles into the air, creates health problems and loss of valuable nutrients. The list of deficient nutrients has lengthened from single element of nitrogen to phosphorus, potassium, zinc, sulphur, boron and manganese (about 8) in a short period of four decades.

Scientific investigations are called upon for each element to know precisely rate of their supply as a function of time so as to predict when, what and how much additional fertilizers will be required. With increasing number of deficiencies optimal ratio of the nutrients will become the driving force for optimizing productivity and sustainability.

As per the latest estimates, energy and water are becoming most critical inputs globally and both of them are intimately co-related to the soil resources. In addition to demographic growth, urbanization rate of 10-11% during 1900 in Asia is at present about 25-30% and is further going to escalate to 50% by 2050. Most of the energy production and consumption is environmentally degradative. High urbanization is likely to produce large quantities of solid wastes, domestic and industrial effluents which will be recycled in peri-urban agriculture. Chemical compositions of these bio and industrial wastes is changing very rapidly due to the production and consumption of a large variety of pharmaceuticals, soaps, sanitation products, industrial processes, etc.

Lack of appropriate treatment technologies and public investments will increase possibilities of contaminating lands, vegetation, vegetables, feed, food and will disrupt natural resources-animal-human consumption chain. The alternative treatment processes of giant scavengers of super microbes and vegetation to clean up land resources in cost competitive and effective manners should be made economically feasible.

Soil is being looked upon as unexplored great gene pool especially after the successful deployment of Bt genes in various crops and commodities. So far there was a very subdued interest and investments on the explorations of soil microbes, their characterization, DNA finger printing, quantifying structural/functional genomics and documentation. This new phase of interests, of course, will be destined by the rapidly growing intellectual property and geographical indicator rights. However, there are very few and adequately trained scientists who can do full justice to the emerging potentials of soil micro-biology. The top most priority will be developing appropriate human resources to compete in the market driven R&D portfolio. At the same time the nano-technologies are going to obliterate rigid boundaries between physical, chemical and biological sciences. Silicon chip of the fastest computers processors may be replaced by the bio chips with billion time's higher speed of conducting messages and telecommunication services matching the speed of human imagination and soil scientists may watch their partnership possibilities.

Climatic and weather changes have now been accepted even by the strongest opponents irrespective of the reasons behind their opposition. If this trends continuous there is going to be redistribution of water on the land, major changes in rainfall patterns, a larger shift in the cropping and farming systems and land uses.

This will also make significant impact on the soil erosion, land degradation, soil microbes and aggradation processes of a very great scientific challenge. In the scheme of mitigation strategies again soil has to play a vital role both as a sink and partial source of global warming. However, some of the puritan soil scientists become upset when we propose renaming of soil science institutions as NRM organizations. At the other hand possibilities of an outrageous inter-disciplinarity with the sciences of nano technology, bio technology, functional and structural genomics are appearing in the horizons.

There is a strong case to re-look or revisit syllabus, curricula and contents of teaching, research and education in the field of soil science so as to respond to the emerging potentials and opportunities of demographically active and knowledge enriched societies of the Asia and other developing regions.

◆

Anthropogenic soil science driven by social demands

Xuezheng Z. Shi

State Key Laboratory of Soil and Sustainable Agriculture, Institute of Soil Science, Chinese Academy of Sciences, Nanjing 210008, China. E-mail xzshi@issas.ac.cn

Throughout the history of soil science over the past 100 years, two factors boosted the development of the science and should not to be ignored: social demands and improvements of theories and technologies related to soil science. The former is the most essential factor for affecting and orienting the development of soil science. As developing countries move toward industrialization, studies of soil science must satisfy dual social demands: to maintain a steady increase in crop production ensuring adequate food supplies and to address environmental and pollution problems raised by rapid industrialization and agronomic development. China is faced with both of the aforementioned demands. Therefore soil scientists in China should urgently initiate the following studies:

Soil resource information

China's national economy has been rapidly developing over the past 20 years due to the implementation of both political and global trade reforms. However, the influx of farming chemicals, changes in farm management systems, and rapid industrialization and urbanization resulted in a proliferation of small-land pieces on which rural landowners manage various crops planted on very small farmland pieces. In China, industrialization has occurred even in small towns and villages with limited land area. For instance, nearly 400 factories have been set up in a small western suburban area (8 km²) of a city in Jiangsu Province. Environmental degradation worsens when such factory locations are intermixed with farmlands. As such, soil properties and pollution levels may change dramatically even across very short distances due to concentrated industrialization and human activities. Consequently, the original soil development factors, formed under natural soil genesis conditions, have been greatly altered in response to this human and industrialized activity. Therefore, in an effort to accurately maintain soil resource inventories, it is imperative that new soil developmental factors (including modern soil use, pollution issues, etc.) be devised. The development of such updated factors will lead to the creation of sound theoretical and methodological frameworks for soil resource information acquisition. To be successful, this will require new academic thought and new techniques to meet evolving social needs.

Soil changes

Following contemporary soil survey methods, pedologists can direct farmers in their cropping practices after they have finished field surveying and sampling, completed laboratory analyses, and mapped the area in advance. However, this raises several important questions: is it necessary to sample an entire field impacted by industrialization and urbanization in order to determine impacts to soil resources? How should the sampling density be determined? At what temporal scale should re-sampling be completed? While answers to many of these questions are available in soil textbooks, these problems have become increasingly difficult to predict and solve. It is quite simple to address the aforementioned problems; that is, only to determine what factors play a major role in addressing soil quality evolution. However, due to a lack of established theory in this field, numerous problems arose and lots of money was wasted when soil environmental quality surveys were compiled in China. For example, when such a survey was conducted over a large area, a large part of the budget had to be used for grid sampling over the entire area. Costs were compounded by laboratory analyses of routine soil properties, heavy metal contents, and various organic residues. The conclusions derived from such projects were often "heavy metal pollution impacts only isolated locations across the sampled area". Yet, lots of money had to be used to arrive at such conclusions. If the major controlling factors for the soil properties, heavy metal contents, and various organic residues were known at that time, a large amount of expenses, manpower, and facilities might have been saved.

Soil classification

This is an old, yet unresolved topic. A soil's unique classification serves as the foundation for rational soil resource utilization, scientific management, and as an indispensable media for international exchange of soil research results. It is a great pity that no internationally unified soil classification system is available to date; though two influential systems, US Soil Taxonomy and the WRB, constitute a large portion of contemporary soil classifications worldwide. In China, soil classification systems have undergone several great changes, resulting in two parallel classification systems currently in use: The Genetic Soil Classification of China (GSCC) and Chinese Soil Taxonomy (CST). Various soil survey achievements at the national, provincial (municipality or autonomous region) and county levels along with a large quantity of soil physical and chemical data in China are reported on the basis of the GSCC. Communication problems arise when a Chinese scientist travels abroad or a foreign scientist comes to China for international soil academic exchange or research because no unified national soil classification system in China is available. Thus the establishment of an internationally unified soil classification system is of paramount importance.

129

At the very least, we should do our best to establish a reference system among the various classification systems so as to meet the needs of soil science development.

In short, soil scientists should not focus their studies solely on soil attributes, but should place emphasis on studies driven by social demands as well. Under powerful human influence, processes of soil change which historically took thousands of years will now occur in only a fraction of that time. So how can soil scientists hope to meet the social demands for soil science development if they ignore anthropogenic soil studies driven by social demands in the early 21st Century?

Acknowledgements
I gratefully acknowledge support from NSFC, the Key Innovation Project of CAS and Knowledge Innovation Program of CAS, and thank Dr. Y. C. Zhao for his help in preparing the manuscript.

◆

The future of soil science

Don Sparks
University of Delaware, Newark, DE 19717-1303, USA. E-mail dlsparks@udel.edu

As President of the International Union of Soil Sciences, I have had the wonderful opportunity to travel around the world the last four years. My travels have taken me to North and South America, Europe, Asia, and Australia. I have met many soil scientists as well as scientists in a number of other disciplines, and also interacted with policymakers. I have been very pleased to see many young soil scientists at the meetings I have attended. This is very important because they are the future of our discipline. Overall, I must say that I am extremely optimistic about the future of soil science. While we have many challenges ahead of us, the opportunities are limitless.

The challenges and issues that nations around the world face are similar. They include: the need for increased food production, increased urbanization, land degradation due to erosion and desertification, land use issues, global climate change, air and water quality, water supplies, food security, and population growth. Every one of these topics is connected to soils and soil scientists must be at the table to help address them. To successfully address these areas we must combine advances in technology with multidisciplinary, interdisciplinary and multifaceted approaches and interactions. While we need to maintain our identity as soil scientists and as a discipline, we cannot work in isolation if we are going to successfully address complex research and societal needs. We must collaborate with colleagues in many fields including mathematics, physics, chemistry, geology, engineering, the social sciences, economics, and ethics and public policy. We must also carry out studies over a range of spatial and temporal scales.

While we have wonderful opportunities, we face a number of challenges. The two I am must concerned about are dwindling funding for soil science, and indeed for most of science, and what I perceive to be a decreasing interest on the part of graduate students to pursue academic careers. To my mind, the two are linked. Many students see their advisors spending more and more of their time "fundraising", often to no avail. The increasing need to chase money in whatever area it happens to be in is a dangerous trend. The days when one could pursue an area of research for many years, and dig deeply into the topic and make major advances, are becoming almost a thing of the past. Additionally, the lack of recurring funds means that some critical areas of research are not being addressed. The lack of emphasis that most countries are placing on research funding is a trend we must reverse.

What then must we as soil scientists do? In my view, we must take a number of pivotal steps in the years ahead. These include: becoming more proactive and effective in communicating to policymakers and the public about issues that we are experts in, and being more aggressive in seeking and advocating for funding to address important agricultural and environmental issues and to enhance the global economy; improving our "image" with scientists in allied fields by publishing and presenting papers in an array of journals and scientific venues; becoming more active in disseminating educational materials and providing training workshops to teachers and students in K-12 so that more students can be attracted to and excited about soil science as an academic major and career; enhancing student recruiting and training efforts at the graduate level; and increasing the diversity of our professional societies in terms of gender, ethnicity, gender, and type of member (we need to reach out more to practicing professionals and ensure that we provide them with membership services that meet their needs). If these steps are taken, I am confident the future of soil science will be bright.

◆

The future of soil science

Roger S. Swift

Faculty of Natural Resources, Agriculture and Veterinary Science, University of Queensland, Queensland, 4343, Australia. E-mail rswift@uqg.uq.edu.au

When soil scientists ask themselves questions such as 'What is the Future of Soil Science?' it usually means that the subject is confronting problems in relation to its continuing importance, the number of soil scientists in key research organisations and the future demand for trained graduates and technicians. Soil science is experiencing such a period of self doubt in a number of countries. I have seen many articles and letters bemoaning the impending fate of soil science and the stupidity and myopia of governments for allowing this to happen. Is soil science in trouble – well, yes and no, depending on where you are in the world. Is soil science still relevant in the modern world? – yes, of course it is. Let me explain why I give these responses.

It goes almost without saying that soil science has made massive contributions to improving agricultural production and guiding land use, and to understanding and managing landscapes and the related ecosystems and environmental process. The great majority of these contributions have been made in a period of around 70 years in the 20th century. It is against this background of high activity and major contributions that we assess the current situation and we need to be aware of this when making judgements.

The declining demand for soil scientists is in developed countries and, if truth be told, we have to admit that this is because many (but by no means all) problems have been solved and some activities have been transferred to private enterprise. In other words, some of the current changes result from the past successes of soil science. Our concern is that the loss of existing soil scientists and the failure to train new ones will mean that these countries will not have the staff and resources to deal with the remaining problems and, more importantly, with new ones which are on their way.

On the other hand, if we look at the nations with emerging economies in S.E. Asia, S. America and parts of Africa, we see many young scientists eager seeking to make their contribution. Our concern here should be to ensure that these young people are able to access the levels of training and resources that they need in order to be successful. European countries, the USA and Australasia have played a large role in the training of soil scientists from developing countries and it is perhaps time to further develop these interactions for the benefit of both groups and to ensure that precious skills and knowledge are passed on and not lost. In this way, both groups will benefit.

As to the future - what are the key issues that confront soil science? We constantly and correctly cite the production of food, fuel and fibre for an ever-growing world population as our overriding responsibility but, despite many dire predictions to the contrary, the production systems still manage to cope somehow. However, we know that soil and water resources are finite, that strains are being placed in the system and that, at some stage, one or more of these will prove to be a key limiting factor.

For example, the amount of high-quality arable land is limited and to overcome this limitation large areas of native forest are being cleared and burnt in America and S.E. Asia for crop or animal production. These clearing activities have major implications for carbon cycling, soil erosion and air pollution (particularly in Asia). The rapidly growing demand for animal rather than plant protein in emerging economies places even greater pressures on the area of productive land required.

In addition to the demands of food production soil scientists will have a role to play in major environmental problems resulting from the redirection of industrial processes as well as the impact of new scientific developments on plant and animal production. Some of the more likely new developments and their implications for soil science are given below. These developments will increase the competition for land use and will require the establishment of sound scientific principles to guide these allocations.

Climate change
Dealing with problems arising from the changes in temperature, water availability and the relocation of agro-ecological zones onto different soil and land systems.

Carbon sequestration
Exploiting the potential to sequestration carbon in trees and in soil organic matter to help ameliorate the carbon dioxide levels in the atmosphere.

Biomass for energy
Producing large amounts of biomass for conversion to liquid biofuels to reduce the reliance on petroleum and the impact of this on soil organic matter levels.

Genetically modified plant
The use of GM plants to produce specific biochemicals to replace petrochemicals as the basis for the production of pharmaceuticals and biopolymers and the need to identify the soils and agronomic systems to produce such plants.

Waste disposal and re-use
Large and highly-concentrated human populations linked with greater environmental awareness and stricter regulations have resulted in major issues relating to the disposal and re-use of solid and liquid, organic and inorganic waste materials with disposal onto soil as the preferred option. Finding ways to achieve this without compromising the long-term health and quality of the soil represents major challenges for soil scientists.

Analysis and instrumentation
New approaches to soil analysis will be developed. These will include the development of techniques for analysis of soil properties *in situ* by remote observation from aircraft or satellites or for the rapid instrumental analysis of soil samples without the need for extraction or digestion. Also the use of global positioning and digital terrain modelling will be common place in agriculture and land management.

So is there a future for soil science? – my answer is yes of course there is. The incomplete list above identifies a number of major challenges sufficient to excite any budding soil scientist and no mention was made of fertility, acidity, sodicity etc. all of which require more attention. There will be a change in the way of working with more emphasis on multi-disciplinary teams who will be required to analyse, interpret and integrate large amounts of data which simultaneously monitor with different parts of the environment or production system. There will be no shortage of challenges and opportunities for soil scientist, let us make sure that there are enough soil scientists to take up the challenges.

◆

The scope of pedology

Victor Targulian
Institute of Geography, RAS, Moscow. E-mail targul@centro.ru

Among all branches of soil science pedology (or genetic soil science in Russian sense of term) is the core, the most basic part of soil science at the interface between earth and life sciences. Pedology allows us to understand the soil as a specific natural body, a bio-abiotic open system and the earth sphere (the pedosphere). It is based on the main pedological paradigm, which defines a soil as an *in situ* formed natural entity according the formula: S = f (cl,o,r,p,t). Pedology studies soil formation and evolution, soil system behaviour in time and distribution in space, and tries to classify the whole diversity of world soils. Basic pedology studies the existing present-day pedosphere everywhere on the land surface. Ideally, this study should be intimately linked with the natural and anthropo(techno)genic environments. The most wide-spread approach applies the famous Dokuchaev-Jenny-Gerasimov triad: factors→processes→features. The main difficulty in empirical and theoretical use of the triad stems from interpreting it too temporally, thus taking into account mainly recent existing factors and processes of soil formation and less attention during other periods of pedogenesis. Our conventional pedogenic concepts for so called "zonal" soils are mainly monogenetic, whereas we understand more completely that the real "history" of the majority of world soils is polygenetic.

The study of the "present-day" pedosphere from a pedological point of view should be process-oriented research targeted to an understanding of specific pedogenic processes which formed the existing diversity of the world soils and may direct soils evolution (development, or degradation) in the future. This kind of research usually starts with the detailed investigation of a set of the stable soil features and characteristics, both morphological and analytical, on all hierarchical levels of soil body organization. A pedological understanding of these features includes their division into the relic irreproducible ones inherited from parent materials, or from the past stages of soil evolution, and into the contemporary reproducible ones, which are produced by existing factors and current pedogenic processes.

On this basis the pedogenetic working hypotheses are elaborated to reconstruct and explain soil formation, development and evolution in time. These hypotheses are constructed from our empirical and theoretical knowledge about specific pedogenic processes (SPP) and allow us to create for each studied soil its process-oriented "portrait". The combination of such portraits with the existing paleogeographical knowledge allow us to describe a soil's genesis including both the set of SPP's and their distribution in time. The main research goals in such studies are the cognition of the biogeochemical and mineralogical essence of the SPP's, their rates and characteristic times, trends and sequences through the time of pedogenesis and their individual inputs into the overall existing pedogenic results – soil bodies and the soil cover.

In the Holocene pedosphere we need to understand step by step the roles, inputs and relationships between the current reproducible pedogenic processes and features and the inherited features which were created by pedogenic processes that have been terminated or even became extinct and therefore are irreproducible.

An understanding of the combined actual and prior evolutionary processes of the triad factors→processes→features is very significant for wise soil management and conservation. We also have the possibility to build the process-oriented forecasts and scenarios of soil systems behaviour in the future under the different types of natural and/or anthropogenic influences.

The major part of pedology as a basic science has been built historically from the knowledge of genesis, evolution, geography and classification of the present day natural soils, exposed on the land surface. This part of pedology could be referred to as present-day natural pedology. During the last decades many other areas of pedology have been developed in response to the challenges of natural sciences and society. One of the most successful is paleopedology which claims sometimes to be an independent earth science. The main success of paleopedology is connected with the study of the Pleistocene and Holocene natural paleosols, both buried and exposed on land surface. Now paleopedology is also studying pedological conditions of much more ancient times: the Meso-Paleozoic paleosols. Describing and understanding of such paleosols has relied mainly on an actualistic approach. But Mesozoic and especially Paleozoic eras had quite specific biotic and climatic environments, many of which became extinct and have not been repeated in the recent biosphere and pedosphere. Consequently, there are more uncertainties to reconstruct the genesis and evolution of extinct soils and pedogenic processes which were associated with extinct types of biota and climate.

Combining the rich results of the Holocene and Pleistocene paleopedology with the first results of Cenozoic and Meso-Paleozoic paleopedology it is possible to consider evolutionary paleopedology and to study and describe the paleosols, paleopedospheres and pedogenic processes of the main stages of the Earth's geological history.

In close connection with the natural paleopedology and present-day pedology, the pedoarcheology or archeopedology has been developing very actively during the last few decades. The study of Palaeolithic, Neolithic and younger archaeological sites, including even some medieval settlements, involves many discoveries and questions concerning paleoanthropogenic soils, pedosediments and pedocomplexes. The scope of this branch of pedology is very large because of rapid expansion of the areas and diversity of the archaeological investigations. A similar expansion is taking place in the study of anthropo-techno-genic soils and pedosediments (anthrosols, technosols, chemozems, urbanozems etc.). In all these cases the implementation of the pedogenetic process-oriented paradigm (factors→processes→features) gives us the possibility to explain the existing set of features and to predict probabilistically the future behaviour of these bodies in time (technopedology).

Another exploratory branch of general pedology is the pedology of Earth regoliths and saprolites which is tightly connected with the ecology, geology, hydrology and hydrogeology of the so-called critical zone of the landscape. Again the process-oriented genetic approach of pedology facilitates predictions of the behaviour of this zone under the various impacts.

Perhaps the youngest branch of pedology is the study of extraterrestrial regoliths of the planets (Moon, Mars, Venus). The first papers about "lunar soils" have already been published. Such researches can help explain how different planetary regoliths are transforming *in situ* under the very severe environments of these planets. Although soil formation is formally impossible without the biota and water, *in situ* formation of a vertically-anisotropic sequence of horizons (or on-site soil-like body, or "siton") recording the impact of severe planet environments – could be quite possible. I believe that the tree of general pedology includes the above branches and that our common theory can be applied to the diversity of pedogenesis and that they encompasses.

Finally I would like to stress that the proper application of the main paradigms, principles, and methodologies of pedology allow us to answer what and how soil-related phenomena are created, and how they will behave in time and space under different impacts.

♦

The future of soil science

Lamourdia Thiombiano

Food and Agricultural Organization (FAO), Regional Office for Africa Accra, Ghana.
E-mail Lamourdia.Thiombiano@fao.org

The *Bororo* people from Ethiopia in East Africa in their daily greetings, first say *"I wish your soil be fertile"*. This picture shows clearly, the sacred consideration they have for soils which are from their perspective, the basic requirement for life and for an equilibrium between human societies and the surrounding environment. A fertile soil is a living soil, at temporal and spatial scales, a provider of food and other spiritual, cultural and environmental benefits for human beings.

A sacred body part of life cycle, soils and lands have always been considered as such, by rural societies all over the world. When a soil is invaded by weeds or is "dying" because of severe erosion, Texan farmers as well as the Russian or European farmers feel badly. In the same vein, for farmers in the developing world, this situation is an illustration of laziness and absence of care for this living body. To protect the soils against these features, the Polynesian farmers do use total and permanent soil cover, a century practices in the region, to produce cocoyam in valleys. These examples show how soils have always been subject of concern, of interest for rural people everywhere; and for urban and peri-urban populations, we just have to quote "no Society even those who are the most maritime, could escape from being rooted from the soils; support of life, soils are by essence". As we all know, buildings, roads, airports and many other infrastructure, essential for urban life, not mentioning the food consumed and the surrounding environment, are all rooted from the soils.

Despite this essential role of soils and lands, there is no substantive investment and strong policy will that could be noted at global level, in support to soil care and proper land use planning, particularly in the developing regions. Soils and lands are taken for granted and are seen like mines, from which you just have to extract or use the products or functions needed for human consumption and welfare.

One of the most alarming consequences of such perceptions and lack of appropriate actions is the current trend of land degradation and desertification, soils and water pollutions, decreasing biodiversity, increasing of natural disasters such as floods and drought, increasing of river sedimentation process and diminution of groundwater volumes, decreasing of soil productivity and increasing of rural poverty in developing countries, etc.

In this context, what could be the future of soils and soil science? The future of soils is in the strengthening of the general perception that they are finite goods, which reveal through their status and trend, our culture and values, as well as the level of consideration and care we could have for Earth. In seeking better future for soils, soil scientists as the most enlighten stakeholders should demonstrate the need to come back to original values of agriculture and friendly natural resources management practices, such as using appropriate tools which minimize soils disturbance and that could keep the soils covered; all together making these soils, more willing to produce our goods and maintain our environment.

The future of soil science is in its presence going through IUSS strong lobbying, in global and important fora at the United Nations and regional bodies levels, when Conventions and policies on natural resources management are discussed, as well as at national levels, during agricultural and environmental policies formulation and implementation. Soils and land issues should be brought back on the Agenda and more clearly tackled in these various Conventions and Millennium Development Goals, ranging from the UNCCD dealing with desertification to Climate change, International waters protection and poverty alleviation. Soil science should linked the better understanding of soil functioning and services with the development of policies and regulations on food security achievement and sustainable natural resources management.

Investing in soils and land care is an important prerequisite for yielding food for all and an ecological balance whilst ensuring benefits from environmental services. The future of soils is in the growing carbon credit markets, which could provide additional means to develop and maintain the vitality of soils. Soil science should stand ready to develop tools for policy advice, curricula for rural communities and local policy makers training, as well as curricula for building capacities of specialists in soil carbon sequestration issues.

The future of soil science is in avoiding to be marginalised in this era of computerizing technology and biotechnology and "high speed" development. Appropriate tools for investigating and capitalizing soil information, assessing, monitoring and forecasting changes in environment and land uses should be part of soil science scope. A more flexible, timely and cost benefit effective approach building on endogenous knowledge, generating new knowledge, tools, practices and advices, which are problems solving with prospective components is needed. New areas such as the status and functioning of lands implanted with land mines in warded countries, the impact of global trade on soil qualities, the ecosystem and river basin approaches, soil biodiversity in connection with the use of GMOs, landscape design etc. should be more vigorously included in soil science domain.

The future of soil science is in its capacity to move from a classic approach and responsiveness based on thematic clusters, to a more coherent and integrated one, based on a good communication skill within multidisciplinary teams dealing with environmental issues, food safety, good agricultural practices, disasters risks forecasting, assessment and management, climate change modelling, etc.

Particularly, in Africa where almost 80 to 90 % of soil institutions from national Universities to Agricultural Research and Development systems are no more very active, there is an imperative for a total mind change, to adapt to the current context needs, in terms of new frontiers for soil information, policy advices and land management options and tools. To give more impetus to soil science, there is a need to develop an appropriate strategy which could be based on the following three principles:

1. Respond to demand driven information, tools and practices and anticipate on priority area for interventions;
2. Develop multidisciplinary skills and a strong IUSS networking and lobbying systems;
3. Strengthening products and services (including policy advices) oriented approach.

The future of soil science is bright; the day policy makers and land users will be asking in their greetings about the fertility and soil health, like the *Bororo* people traditionally do this!

♦

Soil inventory in transition: from too few to too many geo-data ?

Marc Van Meirvenne

Department of Soil Management and Soil Care, Ghent University, Belgium. E-mail marc.vanmeirvenne@ugent.be

As soil scientists we share the problem that our medium of interest is difficult to observe continuously, both in 2- or 3-dimensions. Traditionally we dig pits or auger holes to sample it and complement these observations with indirect information obtained from relationships with visible landscape features or use other inventories like topographic maps. The result is that our inventories are uncertain, to a much larger extent than maps of most other natural phenomena. To reduce the data volume we had to classify the observed properties resulting in complex legends which are then difficult to interpret by non-soil scientists. The consequence is that in respect to the efforts we put in our maps, we feel that they are often underused. Improving this situation has been a challenge for soil surveyors and pedometricians for quite some time.

In the past, soil surveys relied strongly on indirect sources of qualitative information like native vegetation, topography, parent material, etc. resulting in the ClORPT paradigm (Jenny, 1941). Soil surveyors investigated soil in a multivariate way, considering many integrated properties and describing their change in depth as soil horizons. So, typically the legend of a soil map was qualitative, multivariate and three dimensional. But the hard data support of these maps was usually very limited, often restricted to a number of selected soil profiles which were then sampled in detail. Although this approach was sufficient to provide qualitative information, it soon became insufficient as a source for detailed quantitative data required to support soil and environmental management decisions.

In the 1980s and 1990s, the availability of computers and the developments of process simulation models caused a need for quantitative data stimulating studies on the spatial variability of soil properties. This resulted in intense and detailed soil sampling campaigns, complemented by advanced interpolation procedures provided by developments in geostatistics and GIS. Yet despite the increased processing power, most of these studies remained univariate and 2-D. Only some exceptions explored multivariate interpolations (and even then, most remained bivariate) or incorporated the third dimension. In the near future I expect that this evolution will continue towards quantitative, multivariate soil inventories in 3-D.

New and exciting possibilities are offered by the increasing availability of auxiliary data sources, often with full coverage, mainly due to evolutions in GPS-based georeferencing and sensing technologies. Images obtained through remote sensing are increasingly available at smaller spatial and temporal resolutions. We are not far anymore from the situation where civil unmanned aerial vehicles can be directed to scan an area with a resolution of the size of an individual plant (like a sugar beet or a potato). These will become powerful sources of information to monitor crop growth and soil fertility. Additionally, harvest monitors increasingly provide yield maps representing crop performances. At present some farmers have multi-year recordings of these georeferenced harvest data allowing the validation of dynamic crop-response models. Accurate digital elevation models allow to obtain detailed information on the topographic complexity and are very useful to quantify soil-landscape relationships. Promising are the developments in soil sensors because they can provide detailed information about a number of soil properties like salinity, texture, pH, compaction, moisture content, organic matter content, etc. Since some of these are non-invasive, they are flexible to use and can provide a density of observations beyond the capacity of traditional soil survey procedures. Especially measuring the electrical properties of soil seems to be promising for a range of applications. Undoubtedly, in the near future more diverse types of soil sensors will become available and offer new opportunities.

An important phase of data screening and geo-processing is usually needed prior to the extraction of useful soil information from these auxiliary sources. For example, Ping and Doberman (2005) documented in detail the steps of a flowchart to post-process yield data into useful maps: data screening, standardization, interpolation, classification, filtering and interpretation. Sometimes the number of available sensor data might be overwhelming, being much larger than the required resolution. We recently obtained > 50 000 EC_a measurements within an area of 50 by 60 m, where our final map needed a resolution of 0.5 by 0.5 m, which resulted in 4 times less cells. So, besides techniques for interpolation and estimation, we also need methods for filtering, image processing, pattern recognition, selecting the most suitable sources and integrate them in 3-D. Therefore mathematical and statistical techniques for handling large numbers of geo-data, allowing data reduction, modelling multiple coregionalizations using strongly varying numbers of observations and numerical classification will need to be developed further and become more tailored towards the complex soil system.

We are currently in a transition, where we move from problems related to setting up a sampling and interpolation strategy under data poor conditions, to the selection and filtering of multiple sources of auxiliary quantitative information complemented by a limited number of directed soil observations. In summary, I believe we will evolve from a past with too few to a future with too many geo-data. As soil scientists we should be prepared to face this shift and ensure that we have the knowledge and methods available to take full advantage from this new evolution to understand and manage our soils better.

References
Jenny, H., 1941. Factors of soil formation. McGraw-Hill. New York.
Ping, J.L. and Dobermann, A., 2005. Processing of yield map data. Precision Agriculture 6: 193-212.

♦

Ideas on the future of soil science

György Várallyay

Research Institute for Soil Science and Agricultural Chemistry (RISSAC) of the Hungarian Academy of Sciences, Budapest, Hungary. E-mail g.varallyay@rissac.hu

The most important criteria for the quality of life are: healthy and good quality food, and food security; clean water; and a pleasant environment. These are closely related to rational land use and sustainable management of soil resources. Society's awareness towards soil quality is not in accordance with the significant multifunctional role of soil resources.

Soil is a conditionally renewable natural resource; reactor, transformer and integrator of the combined influences of other natural resources (solar radiation, atmosphere, surface and subsurface waters, biological resources), place of „sphere-interactions"; medium for biomass production, for food, fodder, industrial raw material and alternative energy; storage of heat, water, plant nutrients and in some cases wastes from various sources; high capacity buffer medium, which may prevent or moderate the unfavourable consequences of various environmental and/or human-induced stresses; natural filter and detoxication system, which may prevent the deeper geological formations and the subsurface waters from various surface pollutants; significant gene-reservoir, an important element of biodiversity; and conserver and carrier of the heritage of natural and human history.

In my opinion the future of soil science depends primarily on the society knowledge and acceptance of these facts, as necessary elements for the quality of life. Society awareness will press the various level decision-makers to pay particular attention and to give priorities to soil-related economical, ecological and social problems. To expand the sustainability concept to land use and soil management is our number one missionary statement. The multifunctionality of soil is determined by the combined influences of soil properties, which are the results of soil processes. All soil-related human activities influence these processes, consequently their control is the main challenge of contemporary soil science and soil management.

Control of soil processes can be: strengthening and helping favourable processes, such as accumulation of organic matter, development or improvement of soil structure and hydrophysical properties; prevention of undesirable soil processes; soil degradation processes: erosion by water or wind; acidification; salinization/sodification; physical degradation (structure destruction, compaction); biological degradation); extreme moisture regime: the simultaneous hazard of waterlogging or over-moistening and drought-sensitivity; nutrient stresses: deficiency or accumulation and/or toxicity of one or more elements in the biogeochemical cycle; environmental pollution:

accumulation or mobilization of various, potentially harmful (or even toxic) elements (or compounds) in air, in water, in soil; or in the biomass of various organisms within the soil–water–plants–animals–human beings food chain; based on high-probability prognoses and forecasts; moderation of undesirable soil processes, reducing their harmful ecological and environmental impacts at lest to a certain tolerable level; correction of the unfavourable consequences of undesirable processes (reclamation, remediation, improvement).

These processes are controllable on the basis of up-to-date databases, giving opportunity to extend point and minute soil information, and having more and more precise and exact information on soil processes, on their influencing factors and on their mechanisms and inter-relationships. In my opinion, some main scientific tasks of future soil science are as follows: to extend point information (profile–horizon–sample) to territorial ones (mapping unit, agricultural field, physiographical region, watershed) with the application of the modern developments in geo-statistics and remote sensing (multi-spectral satellite imagery, etc.); to extend minute information (sampling, laboratory analyses, in situ measurements) to a longer time period (hour, day, week, month, season, year) with the application of modelling; "in situ" or "in vivo" monitoring of soil processes with measurement of soil characteristics with sensors (EC, soil moisture measurements, ion-selective electrodes, etc.) to get an picture on the three-dimensional flow of the soil solution and its spatial and time variability; to get more information on the mechanisms of phase interactions for the understanding of physical, physico-chemical and chemical transport transformation processes in the atmosphere–hydrosphere–pedosphere continuum; to get more physical, chemical and biological information on the micro-environment of plant roots (rhizoplane) for the understanding and quantification of the mechanisms of water and nutrient uptake, as well as of soil–biota–plant interactions; development of up-to-date dynamic soil databases and monitoring systems; development, improvement and verification of the early-warning prognosis and forecast systems for the prediction of soil processes; alternative possibilities and methods for soil process control with special regard to the prevention of undesirable changes, by applying new technologies in biomass production and environment protection.

I sincerely hope that our joint efforts for the future development of a sustainable multifunctional soil science will create societal awareness for our limited soil resources that we will get the opportunity for the realisation of most of our dreams and convincingly formulated tasks.

◆

Future of soil science as one of the geosciences

Jerzy Weber

Agricultural University of Wrocław, Institute of Soil Science and Agricultural Environment Protection, Grunwaldzka 53, 50-357 Wrocław, Poland. E-mail: weber@ozi.ar.wroc.pl or jerzyweber@wp.pl

From ancient times, humanity considered soil as a life-support system crucial for the production of food. Although the importance of soil was well recognized, naturalists and earth scientists ignored soils until the second half of the 19th century, when V.V. Dokuchaev in Russia and E.W. Hilgard in USA developed new ideas on the nature and origin of soil. From that time, new findings contributed significantly to overall knowledge of soils and their management. Especially, the last decades soil research resulted in spectacular achievements, helping to feed the fast growing population. Nevertheless, soil science is a young discipline and there is place for new applications of basic laws of physics and chemistry. From the other hand, soil science can improve the basic knowledge, as well.

The goal of soil science is not only to answer questions how plants grow in soil, how they get their nutrients or why soils are very different. Intercurrent effects of soil management on the environment should be well defined as well, because of eutrophication of ground water or contamination with xenobiotics. Soils are a transformer, regulator, buffer and filter of water, nutrients and other dissolved and dispersed compounds. Biogeochemical carbon dynamics and aspects of the water cycle continue to be focal points. Soil carbon cycling is the most important link between the biogeochemical processes of the earth and the atmosphere. All these circumstances indicate, that soils have to be considered as an integral part of the environment, and soil scientists have to focus on the origin and the distribution of soils in relation to the history of terrestrial systems. It is fundamentally important to understand and predict the effects of human activity on the environment, including pedodiversity and biodiversity, and to integrate our knowledge into a holistic view of the Earth's dynamics and biogeochemical transformations. Furthermore, soils are becoming more and more important for the reconstruction of paleo-environments, e.g. in archaeology and global change. Ancient and buried soils are one of the better proxies for reconstructing past climate and the development of the landscape. Finally, soil scientists can be helpful in providing explanations on regolith and ground data received from space exploration.

Soil scientists have to cooperate with other specialists, especially geoscientists. Many of the 50,000 soil scientists work in agronomic institutions, studying the composition and dynamics of soils and their possibility to increase soil productivity. Around the world soil science is often coupled with agriculture. This is disadvantageous for soil science and the geosciences. Soil science is undergoing a reorientation from mainly agricultural aspects and soil productivity to environmental issues. At the same time soil sciences departments in several universities transformed their names into environmental sciences or environmental protection, natural resources. This is a natural trend, connected with modification of main goal of pedology, aimed to explain the nature and genesis of soils as a natural resource and part of the earth system. Soil science was not perceived among geosciences and was in some kind of isolation for years.

It happens sometimes that soils are objects of investigations of researchers who are not fully prepared to elucidate soil phenomena and processes. This situation has changed when European Geosciences Union (EGU) was founded in 2002. This new interdisciplinary society was established by fusion of the European Geophysical Society (EGS) and European Union of Geosciences (EUG).

The EGU is a dynamic, innovative and non-profit organization, gathered mainly geologists, mineralogists, geophysics, hydrologists, climatologists and other scientists involved in different fields of the earth and planetary sciences, including space. One of EGU units is divisions on Soil System Sciences (SSS), which brings together soil scientists across the globe in the pursuit of the study and understanding of soils, soil distribution, soil behavior and soil management www.copernicus.org/EGU/EGU.html The Soil System Sciences Division does not intend to be European scientific organization coordinating national soil science societies, but is a unit representing soil science among other geosciences organized in frame of the European Geosciences Union. Several national societies (Polish Soil Science Society, Soil Science Society of America, Italian Soil Science Society) expressed an interest to create closer co-operation with SSS. The scientific activity of SSS is organized in frame of the following committees:

- Weathering, soil mineralogy and micromorphology;
- Soil organic matter and organo-mineral interaction;
- Soil and regolith morphology and genesis;
- Soil physics;
- Soil conservation;
- Soil chemistry and biogeochemical cycles;
- Soil biology, microbiology and biodiversity;
- Soil pollution, degradation and remediation;
- Soil, environment and ecosystem interactions;
- Soil as a record of the past.

From 2004, each year SSS is organizing several sessions dealing with different aspects of pedology. At the 2006 EGU meeting in Vienna, April 2006, more than 400 papers were presented including sessions prepared jointly with Hydrological Sciences and Biogeosciences. The EGU division on Soil System Sciences established a Medal in recognition of the scientific achievements of Philippe Duchaufour, awarded by the European Geosciences Union for distinguished contributions to soil science, defined in its widest sense. Philippe Duchaufour Medal was awarded in 2005 to U. Schwertmann from Munich, Germany, and in 2006 to E.A. FitzPatrick from Aberdeen, Scotland.

Close cooperation of soil science with other geosciences is fundamental for its future. From one side, it will enrich an exchange of ideas, considered sometimes from very different point of view. From the other side, soil scientists may contribute significantly to environmental studies. This cooperation would promote further progress in the knowledge of the Earth systems, for future benefits of the geosciences community.

♦

Some reflections on the future of soil science

Gerd Wessolek

Technical University Berlin, Institute of Ecology, Dep. of Soil Protection, Salzufer 12, D-10587 Berlin, Germany. E-mail gerd.wessolek@tu-berlin.de

Most soil related problems are well known within academic circles, and the general attitude towards soil as a common good is gradually changing. Current issues facing the soil science community are discussed during national and international scientific meetings, and "open questions" are usually starting points for new soil research proposals.

In order to summarize the future challenges of soil science, I began with a simple Google-search using the keywords "future, soil science, and scientific problems". Though my search led to hundreds of thousands of links from all over the world, one thing is certain - whenever natural resources are concerned, some authors are fearful, others complacent. The issues are complex because society itself is complex, and the range and effects of human demands on natural resources is extraordinarily large.

Twenty years ago I was invited to the International Dahlem Workshop on Resources and World Development in Berlin, Germany. The goal of the workshop was to assess energy, minerals, water, and other natural resources, and to examine the influences (environmental, technological, economic, political, and demographic) that would affect their availability and use over the next fifty years. While looking back on the workshop and leafing through its 940 page long report, it became clear to me that all the topics of the Dahlem conference are still relevant today. Global warming, for example, has become a prevalent issue of public interest and political discussion. The question of whether or not significant indicators of global warming exist is no longer discussed today. Indeed, soil scientists are actively working on regional consequences of global warming, while insurance companies and even film producers are discovering new possibilities to make climate change profitable.

Compared to the issues discussed twenty years ago, I have the impression that two problems in particular have become more severe. The first is the assessment of renewable and non-renewable energy resources. Our fossil-fuelled civilization and anthropogenic induced global warming prompt the critical question: to what extent should we be concerned? In this context, I am sure that the use of soil to produce energy (and not food!) will become an important subject for discussion. However, the parallel requirements for fuel and food production from plants will lead to new shortages of available land and soil resources in many countries.

The second problem leads in a similar direction - environmental changes arising from resources use. For example, we can observe an increasing worldwide demand of land for housing, settlements, and infrastructures as a result of growing urban sprawl. There are, however, no political, economic, or planning instruments to enhance soil consumption. Until now, scientists are still unable to provide a concrete way to rescue important soil functions, or to give a clear answer as to how much unsealed soil is needed for fulfilling important ecological processes. Further problems include: the carbon dioxide problem, the nitrogen and phosphorus consumption for food production, the increase of waste, the distribution of water resources, and the permanent loss of natural resources and wildlife.

Can we really solve these problems with legislative instruments? Although we've had soil protection laws in Germany for a decade, many problems concerning soil and the environment remain more or less unsolved.

Finally, I'd like to reflect on some ideas concerning the image of soil as regarded by non-soil scientists. For some people soil is only another expression for dirt. More than anyone else, we soil scientists know that soil fulfils manifold ecological functions and is essential for our civilization, cultural heritage and religions (Bachmann, 2001). This immense importance is confronted with a very poor sense of protection, and a failing interest in ecological questions concerning the general public. Consequently, I suggest introducing soil knowledge into national educational programs. For this purpose, it is essential to train soil scientists in soil didactic and to integrate this knowledge into schoolbooks. This is the best possibility to give the field of soil science a better perspective.

Another aspect concerning our discipline is the need to give soil a new, more up-to-date image in addition to its undisputed ecological significance. One suitable way might be the symbiosis of soil, aesthetics, and art. Different approaches to aesthetically dealing with soil have been developed worldwide. To begin with, many land-art projects of the 1960s and 1970s were very successful, but not directly linked to soil. A better example is the Museonder, in the Netherlands. Developed for didactic purposes, this museum is built directly into the soil and is integrated into the national park "De Hoge Veluwe". In addition to scientific aspects of the exhibition, artistic installations establish connections between soil and the outside world. Utilizing the ground as a natural place for anchoring building materials, architecture is perhaps the best example of the aesthetic use of soil. In Berlin, the architect Martin Rauch modernized traditional building methods with clay.

The use of audio-visual media has opened up an inexhaustible field of soil presentation. An example is the documentary film "Memory of the Soil" by the Japanese producer Shiozaki Toshiko. Her aim is to visualize the beauty of soil. It is intended to fascinate the viewers by the long memory of the soil, its traces of life and culture, and the infinite number of colours and structures. The Internet is also a versatile new medium for representing soil. For example, the Chicago Field Museum gives a virtual tour of their very interesting soil exhibition. One can visit individual stations online and call up short films and explanatory information about special fields of soil science, such as microorganisms, etc.

Many approaches of combining soil, art and didactic are possible. My vision is to "collect" as many ideas as possible in order to stimulate a broader understanding and acceptance of soil in a wider community. Thus soil would be also a subject for landscape art and architecture.

References

Bachmann, G., 2001. Terra preciosa: Böden und ihre Wahrnehmung in Kunst und Kultur. http://www.bodenwelten.de/bodenframe.htm (in German).

McLaren, D.J. and B.J. Skinner (eds), 1987. Resources and World Development. Dahlem workshop report No. 6, 940 pp. A Wiley-Interscience Publication.

The Field Museum in Chicago, 2003. Underground Adventure.

Wessolek, G., 2002. Art and soil. Newsletter of the Committee on the History, Philosophy, and Sociology of Soil Science, IUSS, and Council on the History, Philosophy, and Sociology of the SSSA: 10: 14-16.

alchemistic symbol
for the earth

Future of soil science

Markku Yli-Halla
Department of Applied Chemistry and Microbiology, University of Helsinki, Finland.
E-mail *markku.yli-halla@helsinki.fi*

Soil science is a mature science. As no scientific revolution will likely occur in the foreseeable future, soil science continues with its present paradigms. Scientific advances are amendments to the current theories and help understand soil function more comprehensively. The amendments often emerge where the present theories are applied to new environments and to new types of problems and from the interplay between soil science and other sciences. In the lack of new principal theories, soil science education will mostly include transfer of traditional knowledge to the new generations.

Soil science has increasingly different tasks in the developing countries and in the rich industrial world. In the developing countries, soil science will continue to focus on agriculture, maintaining and improving soil fertility and food production. In that part of the world, soil science will therefore continue to have the closest cooperation with plant production sciences. Owing to the occasional or chronic scarcity of food, the justification of soil science will not be questioned there. Scientific work will, however, be often severely limited by the lacking infrastructure and material resources.

The industrial world is generally abundant in food. In these countries, soil fertility has usually increased and soil nutrients, particularly nitrogen and phosphorus, are often considered to cause environmental problems, such as eutrophication of waters. This attitude and the consequent change in the priorities of research funding continue to force soil science to widen its scope and reconsider its research objectives. While taking care of soil condition of agricultural land remains to be a valuable task among soil scientists also in the industrial countries, soil science will shift strongly to investigating other soil uses as well and be transformed to a more general environmental science. In this area, other earth sciences, such as soil geology, ecology, and environmental engineering, which are more well-known to city dwellers will compete hard with soil science for having the privilege of solving the new soil-related problems. The multiple soil functions and the relationships between the soil and society have been much publicized within soil science, as indicated by the titles of many recent conferences and plenty of textbooks called *environmental* soil science. However, this shift has not yet been clearly recognized or admitted outside our own scientific community. While most soil scientists currently in charge do have agricultural backgrounds and identities, our future colleagues have to be more urban in order to adapt themselves to the changing context of our science.

Our science differs much from some other natural sciences such as biology, chemistry and physics that are regular parts of education at schools. Consequently, people are well aware of many other natural sciences but only few know much about soils. Although soil science will probably never get the same status as the other sciences mentioned above, it should be incorporated in the natural science courses of schools more than it is today. If successful, this attempt will help attract qualified high school graduates to realize the working opportunities within soil science and to enrol soil science curricula.

In the universities and research institutes, the few departments of soil science which still exist continue to be merged to other departments, such as environmental or natural resources sciences. As a consequence, soil science loses visibility in the organizational charts. Within the multidisciplinary organizations, filling of every chair becoming vacant has to be justified, not by the general importance of the science as such, but by the prospected productivity of the field. This is often judged simply by the impact factors of journals where papers are published, a criterion disadvantageous to small sciences. Future success of soil science depends heavily on how well we can cooperate in multidisciplinary research organizations, get our ideas incorporated in their research programmes and become known as experts with unique qualifications for managing soil-related issues of all environments. Soil science will flourish if we bring up such themes that are found important also outside our small scientific community. After all, merging soil science departments with those of other sciences may help cross gaps between the sciences.

We need to increase the communication with politicians, administrators, experts of different backgrounds and the general public about soil functions in an understandable way without jargon, and make soil information available to those needing it. Increased interest towards the soil and its many functions is emerging, for example, by the EU Directive of Soil Protection. Making use of databases, GIS and pedotransfer rules, and generating thematic soil maps is essential in responding to the new demand.

Soil science is well equipped to tackle challenges such as world food crisis and global change and whatever soil-related issues may arise in the future. We are living in the attention economy and it is up to ourselves to make it known to others that soil science makes a difference to everybody and is capable of solving problems of our modern society. World Soils Agenda, a resolution of the 17th World Congress of Soil Sciences in Bangkok in 2002, gives useful guidelines.

♦

Biological processes in the rhizosphere: a frontier in the future of soil science

Fusuo Zhang

Department of Plant Nutrition, China Agricultural University, Key Laboratory of Plant-Soil Interactions, Beijing 100094, P.R. China. E-mail zhangfs@cau.edu.cn

Soil is an essential part of the biosphere and the basis for land plantations which is the linkage between inorganic elements and plants through nutrient flow in the food chain. The plant-soil system is one of the most important components of natural and agricultural ecosystems. Nutrient dynamics in plant-soil systems not only reflect the pattern of nutrient flow but also influence food production and quality and the pathways of contaminants in natural and agricultural ecosystems.

In plant-soil systems, the rhizosphere is not only an interface between roots and soils for an individual plant, but is also the centre of interactions among plants, soils and microorganisms, regulating plant communities, adaptation processes and their growth environment (Marschner, 1995; Zhang and Shen, 1999a, b; Zhang et al., 2002). Therefore, rhizosphere processes should be considered as important ecological processes in plant-soil ecosystems (Rovira, 1991). However, plant, soil and microbial components of the plant-soil ecosystem have usually been considered in isolation from one another, as have the relationships between aboveground and underground parts.

In soil science, scientists have been concerned with the development and functions of soils by which large amounts of organic substances are produced, and thus much progress has been made in soil physics, soil chemistry and soil biology. However, limited information is available on biological interactions in relation to efficient nutrient utilization and nutrient cycling, including the interactions between plant shoots and roots, plant roots and soil microorganisms, and also between various groups of microorganisms. The rhizosphere ecosystem can be defined as an ecosystem of energy transfer, material cycling and information transmission caused by various interactions between plants, soils, microorganisms and their environments (Zhang and Shen, 1999a). According to this viewpoint, the rhizosphere ecosystem is characterized by multi-level components ranging from molecular, individual to community levels. Plants play a dominant role in the interactions among plants, soils, microorganisms and their environments due to mass energy input as carbon to the system as proposed by Whipps and Lynch (1986) and Marschner (1995).

In the rhizosphere ecosystem, plants (producers) provide both the organic carbon required for the functioning of the rhizosphere microorganisms (decomposers) and the resources for root-associated organisms such as root herbivores, pathogens, and symbiotic mutualisms. Plants via root exudation and release of specific signalling compounds affect the composition and structure of the rhizosphere community (Marschner, 1995). The microorganisms in turn decompose plant materials such as root exudates, root residuals and straw, and indirectly modify plant growth and plant community composition by determining the supply of available soil nutrients. Root-associated organisms influence the direction and quality of energy and nutrient flow between plants and decomposers. Exploration of the root-soil interface processes at individual, population and ecosystem levels is a challenging area attracting much attention and requires more consideration of the biological interactions in the rhizosphere and also between aboveground and belowground components and their relationships.

In the plant-soil system, rhizosphere processes are the linkage between plant processes and soil processes and, to some extent, determine the exchange of matter and energy between plants and soils and thus affect crop productivity or ecosystem stabilization (Zhang et al., 2002). There is now increasing recognition of the influence of these components on one another and of the fundamental role played by aboveground-belowground feedback, cross-talk of plants to plants, roots to microorganisms, or microorganisms to microorganisms in soils in regulating ecosystem processes and properties.

Therefore, it is very important for optimizing plant production or ecosystem stability to understand rhizosphere interactions, particularly the mechanisms of nutrient flows related to rhizosphere biological processes in plant-soil systems. For these reasons, the management of rhizosphere ecosystems and rhizosphere processes towards sustainable development of the plant-soil system may be one of the most important opportunities to enhance the efficiency of nutrient resource utilization and crop productivity in various cropping systems, and also to sustain both biodiversity and stabilization of natural ecosystems (Zhang and Shen, 1999a).

One of the major research aims of soil science should be focussed on the study of the effects of various biological processes in the rhizosphere. More emphasis should be placed on the following aspects to solve complex questions concerning biological interactions in soils, particularly in the rhizosphere, in association with efficient nutrient utilization and energy flow:

- Plant-induced biological processes in the rhizosphere and interactions among various organisms in the rhizosphere in association with efficient nutrient utilization, plant productivity, and ecosystem stabilization;
- Mechanisms of the interactions between the aboveground and the belowground feedbacks in relation to biodiversity and nutrient flows;
- Interactive mechanisms of biotic relationships as related to abiotic factors to drive community structure and function and ecosystem properties.

References

Marschner, H., 1995. Mineral Nutrition in Higher Plants. Academic Press. London.

Rovira, A.D., 1991. Rhizosphere research-85 years of progress and frustration. In: D.L. Keister and P.B. Cregan (eds.) The rhizosphere and plant growth. Kluwer Academic Publishers, pp.3-13.

Whipps, J.M. and Lynch, J.M., 1986. The influence of the rhizosphere on crop productivity. Advances in Microbial Ecology 9, 187- 244.

Zhang, F. and Shen, J., 1999a. Progress in plant nutrition and rhizosphere research. In: Research progress in plant protection and plant nutrition. China Agriculture Press. Beijing, 458-469.

Zhang, F. and Shen, J., 1999b. The preliminary development of the theoretical concept of rhizosphere ecosystem and its research emphasis, J. China Agri. Sci. Technol. 4, 15-20.

Zhang, F., Shen, J., and Zhu, Y., 2002. Nutrient interactions in soil-plant systems. In: R. Lal (ed.) Encyclopedia of soil science. pp. 885-887, Marcel Dekker, New York.

♦

The future of soil science

Jianmin Zhou

Institute of Soil Science, Chinese Academy of Sciences. E-mail jmzhou@issas.ac.cn

Soils are most fundamental and non-renewable resource, which is regarded by the international policy community as increasingly important in world development issues such as food security, environmental protection, poverty alleviation, restoration of deteriorated land, and maintenance of ecosystem stability (Wood et al., 2000). However, soil science does not have the prominence and visibility in world development as economics and other disciplines. The way soil scientists communicate our knowledge fails to address many of the needs of the international policy community where major decisions about agriculture and environment are made (Sanchez, 2002). With the development of the society, soil science will play more and more important role in meeting an increasing demand of the human being. In pace with the advance of the other science disciplines and the application of the new technologies, soil science will obtain motive power for its development. Soils research will be broadened from production agronomy and basic pedology to a more multifunctional character encompassing production, human welfare and ecosystem functions (Bridges and Catizzone, 1996). Therefore soil scientists will face more severe challenges to make soil science become a major player in future world development (Sanchez, 2002).

Pedosphere and other spheres

Soil is not only the product from the interaction among lithosphere, hydrosphere, atmosphere, and biosphere, but also the pivot of material cycling and energy exchange between these spheres. Soil plays a most important role in maintaining the lives and health of whole ecosystem on the earth. Pedosphere lies on the interface of lithosphere, hydrosphere, atmosphere, and biosphere. Therefore, future soil science should pay more attention to the study on material cycling and energy exchange between pedosphere and the other spheres. The researches will mainly have to focus on i) the influence of intensive land use on greenhouse gases fluxes to and from atmosphere; ii) the exchange of nutrient elements in soil-plant system and their effect on plant growth and product quality; iii) water cycling and solutes movement between pedosphere and hydrosphere and their effect on the quality of terrestrial water; iv) the dynamic changes of soil quality and their effect on soil biodiversity and soil ecological balance.

Agriculture and the environment

Today, people are still facing the threat of food security since the population increases, especially in developing countries. With the fast urbanization and industrialization, the area under cropland is declining. Cereal production depends on the yield increase per unit land to guarantee the food security. As a result, cropland in developing countries must be kept intensively used, and high inputs are inevitable to maintain high yields. This intensive use of the land will affects the environment. Although new techniques will be developed and applied to increase the utilization efficiency of the fertilizers and the other chemicals such as pesticides, it is impossible to avoid the negative effect of the chemicals on the environment. How to keep the optimal balance between agricultural and economic development and environmental protection is a key question. Soil science should supply theory, technology and measures to solve the problems at different scales.

Biodiversity and genomics

Soil is the biggest organism habitat and may harbour most of our planet's undiscovered biodiversity. Therefore soil is the most important gene reserve, containing more biota in species diversity and quantity than all other above ground biomass of the globe (Blum, 2002). The characteristics of soil biodiversity and evolution processes in different regions and management practices will help us to search for the factors which control the distribution and abundance of members of the soil microbial community and to understand how these communities change with time in response to their environment. In pace with rapid progress in biology and biotechnology, soil biology has prospects. Exploitation and application of soil organism resources and their functions has great potential in the future. The soil genomics and metagenomics will become a very active area in soil science. Functional microorganisms and new genes will be applied to different aspects in agricultural production, human health and ecological protection.

Soil quality

An outstanding characteristic of soil quality change is the disturbance of human activities. Maintenance and protection of soil quality under intensive land use and fast economic development conditions become more and more challenged. Facing the change of soil quality, the regular investigation and successive detection of is necessary to assess land degradation and its trends. Soil quality data not only contain soil fertility, but also the indices reflecting environment and human health. Selection of appropriate indices to describe the soil quality needs further study. Attention should be paid to the different degradation processes and corresponding remediation measures, including soil nutrient imbalance and rational fertilization, soil pollution and bioremediation, soil erosion and conservation, and soil allelopathy and

159

avoiding mechanisms. Quantitative and digital description of soil quality change processes will be possibly realized by means of modern information technology and worldwide data bank and network (Mermut and Eswaran, 2001).

Soil science at the micro-scale

The study of variable-charged soils and their effects on transformation and transportation of different elements are very important since these soils are extensively distributed in the tropics and subtropics. Basic soil theories were originated from the studies on the constant-charged soils, therefore not all phenomena in variable-charged soils cannot be explained by traditional theories. The binding energy of different particles probably determines the stability of soil systems. The interactions among soil constituents such as soil minerals, organic matter, micro-organisms, and various elements and their effects on soil fertility and environment need deepening understanding. The behaviour of nutrients and pollutants in rhizosphere is different from that in the bulk soil, whereas most transformation of nutrients in fertilizer usually takes place in the interface between the fertilizer particle and soil. Therefore, research on transformation and movement of soil substances in the rhizosphere and the interfaces between fertilizer and soil is important.

References

Blum, W. E. H., 2002. The role of soils in sustaining society and the environment: realities and challenges for the 21st century. 17th WCSS, Bangkok, pp.67-86.

Bridges, E. M. and M. Catizzone, 1996. Soil science in a holistic framework: discussion of an improved integrated approach. Geoderma 71: 275-287.

Mermut, A. R. and H. Eswaran, 2001. Some major development in soil science since the mid-1960. Geoderma 100: 403-428.

Sanchez, P. A., 2002. Soil science as a major player in world development. 17th WCSS, Bangkok, pp. 55-64.

Wood, S., K. Sebastian and S. J. Scherr, 2002. Pilot Analysis of global ecosystem: Agroecosystems. International Food Policy Research Institute and World Resources Institute, Washington DC.

♦

Epilogue

Alfred Hartemink

ISRIC – World Soil Information, PO Box 353, 6700 AJ, Wageningen, The Netherlands. E-mail alfred.hartemink@wur.nl

This book expresses the views from some 55 soil scientists in 28 countries on the future of soil science – from Finland to South Africa, from Canada to Ghana, Malaysia and China. This book is as much about the future of soil science as about our current thinking about that future. Here is some afterthought, unbalanced and biased perhaps, but a synthesis is needed in any book in which duplications of ideas cannot be weeded out by editing.

Certainly, views differ – both in approach and content. Some are detailed shopping lists of opportunities and activities; others are looking back and extrapolating to the near future. Some are global, others hardly think outside their laboratory, university, country of origin or own subdiscipline. Some are technical and focus on the rhizosphere or fancy technologies; others are general and they could apply to many natural sciences. They are reflective, introspective, responding to a change, defensive; a few suffer from a little self-indulgence or ancestor-worship. In summary, the views on the future of soil science are not homogeneous (thank goodness), but it cannot be denied that some are insulated from the slightest spark of original thinking. Let's have a look at some of differences and similarities.

Some commonalities and differences

There are some common themes or topics. The first, brought up in the great majority of the views, is that soil science cannot work in isolation, needs to be part of multidisciplinary or interdisciplinary teams, and should reach out to other disciplines. This is already happening in many institutions and countries. It brings with it some concern about the identity of soil science and how it should be safeguarded. The identity issue is linked to the second most commonly held view: soil science has been poor in communicating its successes, and several authors believe that interaction with policy makers and the general public needs to increase.

Most people think thematically, that is soil science should contribute to major global issues like for example food production, climate change studies, or environmental impact. There is some relation between the views of a particular person and its whereabouts. Contributions from Western Europe or the USA stress the need for integration of soil science into, for example, environmental studies and soil science needs to go beyond agriculture, as Baveye and many others put it. About a dozen of the 55 contributions are from soil scientists working developing countries and most of them emphasise the importance of soil science in increasing food production and its link to agriculture. Those who have worked in developing countries before (e.g. Lal, Eswaran) also put emphasis on these aspects. The soil science capacity in developing countries is thin as Bekunda and Gachene have mentioned (limited and shrinking soil science capacity) and they urge for increased links non-soil science disciplines. Environmental attention is also mentioned as an area of research that becomes increasingly important in tropical regions where most of the population growth takes place. Clearly, soil science has different tasks in different parts of the world. It will not stay like that in Powlson views, it may change when we approach 8 billion people and agriculture may become important again.

Same old song?

Communication and interaction are not entirely new themes in soil science. Some 15 years ago, Prof. Dennis Greenland wrote the article "The contributions of soil science to society – Past, present and future" (Greenland, 1991):

> "…soil scientists have also been frustrated as their advice has gone apparently unheeded. This may be because the advice is couched in terms more easily understood by other soil scientists than by politicians and economists who control the disposition of land. If soil science is to serve society fully it is essential that its arguments are presented in terms readily understood by all and with both scientific and economic rigor so that they are not easily refuted."

Despite 15 years of progress this sentiment is echoed in most of the contributions in this book. Greenland also said a few things on soil classification and soil degradation:

> "It is hoped that the names of the soil order will in time become as well known as those of the planets and the orders in the plant and animal kingdoms."
> "Soil science has a major contribution to make to society in establishing the facts of soil degradation on a rigorous, scientific basis we well as in clarifying the scale of economic cost that will be needed to rectify the damage where it is possible to do so."

Again, some authors in this book made fairly similar comments on soil classification (e.g. Powlson, Shi) and soil degradation (e.g. Pla Sentis). So given the fact that Greenland made these comments 15 years ago and several of his ideas still hold today, should we be pessimistic? No I think not. There has been progress in many parts of the world bringing soils on the political agenda, for example in the EU (see Dumanski, King, Nieder, Nortcliff) but also in various conventions. That was not there in 1991.

Several authors are not so optimistic. For example, on the ratio between applied work and fundamental soil science. Many notice a drive towards more applied soil science (e.g. McKenzie) which, in the long-term, will be problematic. Several authors also questioned the issue of specialisation versus generalisation (e.g. Burghardt, Bouma). Kalra called the specialisation the fragmentation of our science. Increased specialisation affects soil science's visibility, but it happens in many other sciences (Baveye, 2000; Seitz, 2000) and should not be a concern *per se*. On the other hand, we see that many students taking soil science classes come from different schools (e.g. ecology, biology, toxicology) and are in need of some general soil science education. So, perhaps our science is on a specialising path, but our education is generalizing.

Several people have stressed the importance of education (e.g. Makeschin, Rashid, Sparks). McBratney urges: our numbers need to rise faster; Swift points out: "There will be no shortage of challenges and opportunities for soil scientist, let us make sure that there are enough soil scientists to take up the challenges." This is a difficult area. With limited job opportunities and difficult funding, students may not be wildly enthusiastic.

There were only two contributions from women and Mary Beth Kirkham raised the gender issue. With an increasing number of female soil science students in many universities, the global soil science community may look different in the future. This book provides ample ideas for them. Apart from priorities in standard topics like, for example, soil pollution or soil erosion, there is attention for soils and human health (e.g. Baveye, Frossard), soils in urban areas (e.g. Burghardt, Ibáñez), biodiversity, soil quality, extraterrestrial soils (Targulian), indigenous soil knowledge (Fowler) whereas Thiombiano and Wessolek point out the cultural values of soils. Climate change, environmental issues and food production are mentioned by most authors. Water is mentioned in many contributions (e.g. Minhas, Samra) as a major research area for soil science. Some are optimistic about the digital revolution (e.g. Dobos), others are more careful (e.g. McKenzie, van Meirvenne). Some are optimistic (Kirk); some are less optimistic (Kirkham).

Labelling or re-labelling of our activities is discussed by Lin who argues for the use of hydropedology and the critical zone. Samra viewed this as follows "some of the puritan soil scientists become upset when we propose renaming of soil science institutions." These trends are indeed opposed by Baveye, but not by many others. It seems that apart from the fruitless discussion on pedology vs. soil science not many seem to bother about renaming - perhaps as it has already been completed.

Some other noteworthy items. It is clear that Hans Jenny continues to be influential and he is quoted in 10% of the contributions. When asked in the late 1980s what could have caused his influence, he replied: "I simply outlived my enemies". Alex McBratney posed the question "Isn't it time Jenny was superseded?" Many have argued that soil science follows Kuhn's paradigm path (e.g. Addiscott and Mirza, 1998; Amundson, 1994; Bouma et al., 1999; de Orellana and Pilatti, 1999; Ekins, 1998; Govers et al., 1999; Herrick et al., 2002; McCown, 2001; Sanchez, 1994; Welch and Graham, 1999). If that were true, than McBratney's question is highly valid and undoubtedly throws down a challenge. The question is whether we can seek for answers now so much is geared towards the applications of our science.

It was interesting to note that the "Encyclopedia of Soil Science" (Lal, 2002) has been cited by various authors. Also the "Handbook of Soil Science" (Sumner, 2000) has been quoted but the "Encyclopedia of Soil Science in the Environment" (Hillel et al., 2005) not yet. These books summing up vast soil scientific knowledge mark the end of a generation that is, or will soon be, retired. Perhaps they mark the end of an era, and the beginning of a new one. None of the references cited in the Foreword of this book were cited. Forward looking articles have a short shelf-life; sooner or later they become the present and then they are done, they are the past.

So well...

This book opened with a cautionary quote from Friedrich Nietzsche, which we, as earth scientists, certainly appreciate. But Nietzsche said a few more wise things: "The future influences the present just as much as the past." Let us hope that the future wishes and intentions expressed by various authors in this book do affect our future. The question is whether we as soil science community can determine part of our own future. Can we bend the future in a desirable direction? Several authors believe we can, and I think they are right. Soil science in the future will be different from what we have done so far, it is different from what we do at the moment, but it will be done. Petersen summarised the soil science future so aptly: "The future of soil science is both exciting and challenging. We have never had as many issues for soil scientists to address or as many opportunities for them to investigate as we have in today's society. We are also fortunate because we have a broad array of new technologies available to the soil science community."

References

Addiscott, T.M. and Mirza, N.A., 1998. New paradigms for modelling mass transfers in soils. Soil & Tillage Research, 47: 105-109.

Amundson, R., 1994. Towards the quantitative modeling of pedogenesis - a Review - Comment - Functional vs mechanistic theories - the Paradox of Paradigms. Geoderma, 63: 299-302.

Baveye, P., 2000. To create generalists, teach students how to learn by themselves. Nature, 404: 329.

Bouma, J., Stoorvogel, J., van Alphen, B.J. and Booltink, H.W.G., 1999. Pedology, precision agriculture, and the changing paradigm of agricultural research. Soil Science Society of America Journal, 63: 1763-1768.

de Orellana, J.A. and Pilatti, M.A., 1999. The ideal soil: I. An edaphic paradigm for sustainable agriculture. Journal of Sustainable Agriculture, 15: 47-59.

Ekins, P., 1998. A new paradigm of development for the next century. International Journal of Environment and Pollution, 9: 267-286.

Govers, G., Lobb, D.A. and Quine, T.A., 1999. Preface - Tillage erosion and translocation: emergence of a new paradigm in soil erosion research. Soil & Tillage Research, 51: 167-174.

Greenland, D.J., 1991. The contributions of soil science to society - past, present, and future. Soil Science, 151: 19-23.

Herrick, J.E., Brown, J.R., Tugel, A.J., Shaver, P.L. and Havstad, K.M., 2002. Application of soil quality to monitoring and management: Paradigms from rangeland ecology. Agronomy Journal, 94: 3-11.

Hillel, D. et al. (eds.), 2005. Encyclopedia of soils in the environment (4 vols.). Elsevier, Amsterdam.

Lal, R. (ed.), 2002. Encyclopedia of soil science. Marcel Dekker, New York.

McCown, R.L., 2001. Learning to bridge the gap between science-based decision support and the practice of farming: Evolution in paradigms of model-based research and intervention from design to dialogue. Australian Journal of Agricultural Research, 52: 549-571.

Sanchez, P.A., 1994. Tropical soil fertility research: towards the second paradigm, Transactions 15th World Congress of Soil Science. ISSS, Acapulco, pp. 65-88.

Seitz, F., 2000. Decline of the generalist - The vigour of every discipline depends on people of broad vision. Nature, 403: 483.

Sumner, M.E. (ed.), 2000. Handbook of soil science. CRC Press, Boca Raton.

Welch, R.M. and Graham, R.D., 1999. A new paradigm for world agriculture: meeting human needs - Productive, sustainable, nutritious. Field Crops Research, 60: 1-10.

◆